PANIC
BUTTON

Melodie Chenevert directs her own company, PRO-NURSE, that provides products and services designed to increase professional pride and productivity. She is the author or *STAT: Special Techniques in Assertiveness Training, The Pro-Nurse Handbook, Mosby's Tour Guide to Nursing School*, a survival guide for nursing students; and a coloring book called *I Might Be a Nurse* to introduce children to the many roles nurses play.

As a professional speaker, she has conducted workshops throughout the United States as well as in Canada, England, and Australia, flcusing on communication skills, management strategies, professional issues, creativity and innovation. Her assertiveness book has been translated into French, Japanese, and German.

She received her diploma from Methodist-Kahler School of Nursing in Rochester, Minnesota; her bachelor's and master's degrees from the University of Washington-Seattle; and an MA in Journalism from the University of Wisconsin-Madison. Before forming her own company, she worked as a staff nurse, play therapist/child mental health clinician, instructor in psychiatric nursing, and even set up an entire school of nursing from scratch.

MELODIE CHENEVERT

WHAT NEXT NURSE

The Career Planner for Panic-Stricken Nurses

Publisher: Melodie Chenevert, RN
Executive Editor: Nancy Evans
Production Editor: Ron Bolen, Jr., RN
Cover Design: Cyndie Widmer
Illustrations: Kathy Wilson

Note: The illustrations are part of a coloring book,
I Might Be a Nurse, *which is designed to teach children about the many roles nurses play. It is available from Pro-Nurse Press.*

Printed in the United States of America on recycled paper.

ISBN: 0-9646046-0-4

Of
ten nurses
reading this book
one will stay in nursing
no matter how bad it gets
and
one will leave nursing
no matter how good it gets

this book
is dedicated to
the other eight

SOLEMN VOWS

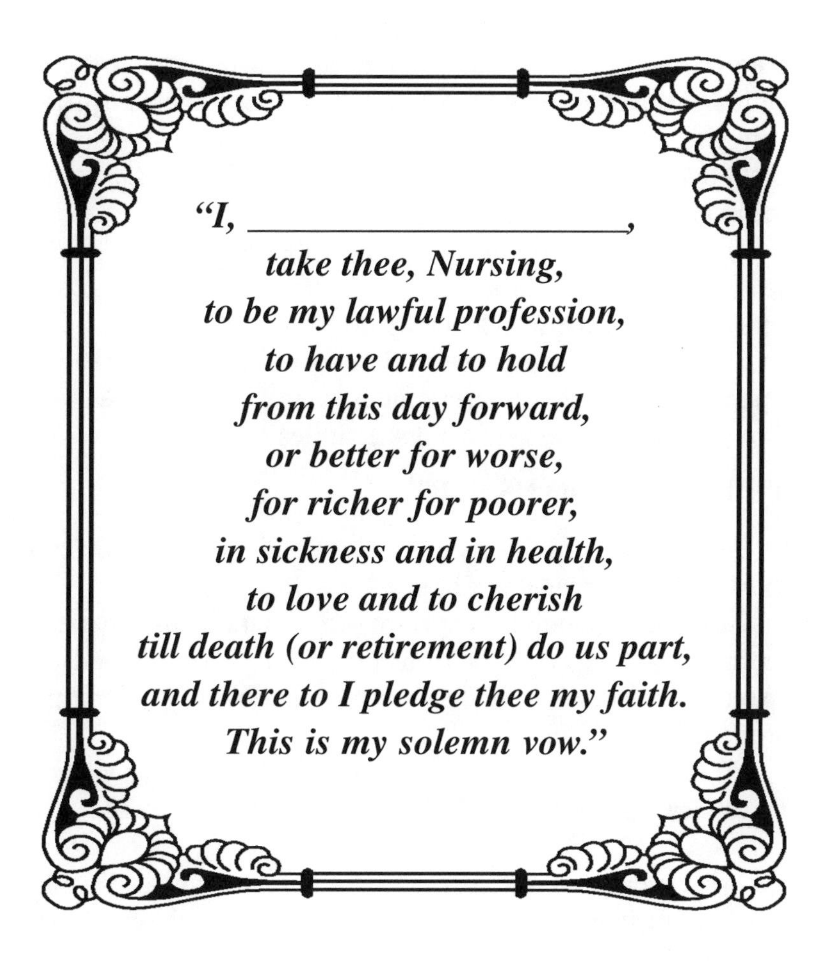

"I, ____________________,
take thee, Nursing,
to be my lawful profession,
to have and to hold
from this day forward,
or better for worse,
for richer for poorer,
in sickness and in health,
to love and to cherish
till death (or retirement) do us part,
and there to I pledge thee my faith.
This is my solemn vow."

Becoming a nurse is like taking a solemn vow. Many of us feel nursing is more than a job, it's a calling. There is a permanence about it. We feel married to it.

Ask your colleagues how they felt about becoming nurses. Be prepared for some fascinating answers.

I'll never forget one delightful nurse who said she really felt "called" to this profession. She was deeply religious and had prayed for direction. She felt God wanted her to be a nurse. She resisted. Nursing was not her first choice. It was not even her second or third choice. But the more she resisted, the more compelled she felt to become a nurse. It was an intense spiritual struggle.

In tears, she confided to a close friend, "I think God wants me to become a nurse."

Trying to comfort her, the friend solemnly replied, "Did he say you had to be a nurse *forever?*"

There was a pause. Then they both burst into laughter.

She's been a nurse for several years now. Whenever she has a particularly tough day, she reminds herself of her escape clause. God didn't say "forever." And she smiles.

TILL DEATH DO US PART

Few get married thinking they will end up divorced. Yet almost half of all marriages fail.

Perhaps we shouldn't expect more of nursing than we do of marriage, but we do. Most of us prefer long-term relationships in our professional as well as our personal lives. We don't play around. We are faithful.

When nurses leave jobs, it smacks of infidelity. When nurses leave nursing, it's the equivalent of divorce.

"My parents introduce me as their daughter who can't hold a job," Sarah says as she rattles off a lengthy series of positions she's held.

After listening to her I suggest she tell her parents, "It's not that I can't hold a job. It's just the opposite. I can hold *many* jobs!"

Sarah is a gifted nurse who is seduced by a challenge. Once she masters a job, she quickly becomes bored. By then her abilities and accomplishments have usually caught the eye of someone who offers her a new challenge. She's off with barely a backward glance.

Sarah's job hopping is making her parents nervous. For them it's almost like "sleeping around." They're afraid she'll ruin her reputation.

Their fears are understandable. They come from an era of long-term relationships. You signed onto a company and you remainded faithful—for better, for worse, for richer, for poorer, in sickness, and in health. Her father, for example, worked for the same company from his late teens until his early sixties, only taking time out to serve in the military.

But what worked for her parents won't work for Sarah. It's not just that they're different people; the times are entirely different.

By seizing opportunities and constantly upgrading her skills, Sarah is staying employable, which in this day and age is much safer than being merely employed. Instead of being embarrassed by their daughter's behavior, they should be proud. Because even if Sarah wanted to remain faithful, chances are she'd be jilted by her hospital.

NAUGHTY, NAUGHTY

Whenever a nurse chooses to walk a new or different path, she feels guilty. Whenever a nurse gets bored or stops giving 150% to her job, she feels guilty.

If you've begun to question your relationship with your job or your profession, this book is for you. While it may not contain all the answers, it will get you started asking the right questions.

This book is about permission:

Permission to leave but the courage to stay.

Permission to stay but the courage to leave.

Whatever you choose—leaving or staying—do it with your whole heart. Remember, what's best for the nurse is what's best for nursing.

Whether you are unemployed or *underemployed,* this book will help you take a fresh look at your career. It will help you figure out where you are coming from and where you are going to.

One of my favorite Far Side cartoons shows a man and woman driving along. The road sign says, "Now Entering the Middle." She is holding a map to "Nowhere" and remarks, "Well, this is just going from bad to worse."

If you've begun to sense things are going "from bad to worse," **Don't Panic!** If you're on the road to Nowhere, turn around. This book will help you get *Somewhere*. This book will help you make your own map so you can get going "from better to best."

TABLE OF CONTENTS

NO-FAULT JOB/CAREER CHANGE

Dissolving a marriage can be an extremely bitter process with each party seeking to sabotage, scapegoat, ruin, and lay blame. "Divorcing" a job or a career can be equally bitter. The relationship between the nurse and her job or profession deteriorates and then disintegrates. Logic and reason evaporate in the heat of anger. Ancient, trivial grievances spring to mind. Everything bad is remembered. Everything good is forgotten. The smallest inconveniences suddenly assume monumental proportions. The final straw may be something as innocuous as being asked to work a double shift, being denied a simple request, or not being consulted before a minor change is made on the unit.

The advent of concepts like "no-fault" or "irreconcilable differences" took some of the vengeance out of divorce. Maybe those same concepts can take some of the pain and bitterness out of making a job or career change. The separation does not have to be done in anger and despair.

NO-FAULT JOB CHANGE

A very good friend of mine, whom I'll call Peggy, was a terrific wife and mother of five. She volunteered her time generously, served the community tirelessly, and when her youngest child entered school, she returned to finish her college degree and get her teaching credentials. While in school she held a part-time job as a teacher's aid which she loved. Upon graduation the job market was extremely tight and it appeared she would not find a teaching position.

Three days before fall term began, she got a frantic call from the school superintendent. There was an immediate need for a fifth grade teacher. Although Peggy wanted to teach kindergarten, she was persuaded to step into the slot. Family and friends encouraged her, saying if she just got into the system, it would open doors for her.

Against her better judgment, she took the job. The next three days were a nightmare as she scrambled to make lesson plans and prepare to simultaneously step into a new job at a new school in a new role. The first day was a disaster. She wept all the way home. Headaches and heart palpitations accompanied her to work the next day. She had crammed into the wee hours hoping to get a handle on everything. The second day was as bad or worse. On the third day, while driving to work, she realized she was fantasizing ways to get out of the mess she'd gotten into. It frightened her to realize she would welcome a major illness or traffic accident, just to get out of teaching.

Feeling both she and her class deserved better, she went to see the superintendent. She told him she was in way over her head and drowning. She said this was so stressful she feared her first year of teaching would be her last. After candidly describing her experience, she asked to be released from her commitment.

The superintendent sat quietly and then said, "Peggy, there's a lot more to life than this job. If this is what is best for you, I will release you from your contract."

When she told her husband what she had done, he was shocked. All he asked was, "What are you going to do with the rest of your life?" She hadn't even thought of that. She just knew she was in the wrong position and she had to get out. Friends were shocked. They were sure she was competent and suggested she should have toughed it out. Colleagues were shocked and worried that she had now scuttled any chance she might have had to get a teaching position.

The next morning she called her former boss and asked if her old teacher's aid position had been filled. Her boss laughed and said, "I suppose you want your old job back?" When Peggy said, "Yes, as a matter of fact, I do," there was a stunned silence. Before she could completely explain what had happened, her boss quickly took her back.

Within two weeks, the school found an excellent fifth grade teacher, much to Peggy's relief. In six months an unexpected opening came up for a kindergarten teacher. Peggy was the first one the superintendent called. She happily accepted. The job was a perfect match for her talents. To this day she loves teaching.

It takes guts to know when to quit. It takes guts to be true to yourself in spite of pressure from others. There was nothing wrong with the first job. There was nothing wrong with Peggy. The two were just mismatched. They did not belong together.

Peggy was in and out of that job so fast it was less of a "divorce" and more of any "annulment." Separation from a job or career may become more difficult with time.

Do you have the guts to quit? Do you have the guts to be true to yourself in spite of pressure from others?

Samantha had been acting department chair in maternal-child nursing for almost a year. The university was pleased with her performance and offered her the position. She declined.

The administrator thought her action was a bargaining ploy. He kept sweetening the pot—more salary, more fringe benefits, more autonomy. Samantha held firm, insisting she loved teaching and wanted to surrender the administrative activities to someone else.

When the administrator realized she was serious, he muttered, "What a waste!" That remark still bothers Samantha.

We've all served time under teachers who would have made better administrators and administrators who would have made better teachers. It is a wise nurse who stays true to herself.

Samantha held to her convictions although she admits she was tempted momentarily. The administrator's confidence in her was flattering and his offer was more than generous.

She says she is sure she made the right decision, adding, "As an administrator, I was adequate. As a teacher, I'm great!"

Just as choosing the wrong mate can sour you forever on marriage, the wrong job can sour you forever on nursing. Before things reach that point, consider a "no-fault" job change.

NEW INFORMATION—NEW DECISION

Every now and then I stumble across a sentence that leaps off the page and burns into my brain. It may be a phrase or a single word that spontaneously unlocks one of life's mysteries and goes on to prove itself useful time and time again.

One of my favorite examples is: "People rarely change their minds, but they will make a new decision based on new information." It was written by Zig Ziglar, a legendary salesman, who was advising other salesmen on how to handle customers.

It's true. We hate to change our minds. It means admitting we were ***wrong***. Or it conjures up other unflattering words like unstable, unreliable, flighty, indecisive, unpredictable, undependable, and, worst of all, inconsistent.

Instead of asking people to change their minds, try giving them a bit of additional information—cite a study, discuss a news report, share the experiences of others in their predicament. Then call for a new decision. It enables a doctor to change his order, a patient to accept treatment, a child to change behavior, or an employee to accept a transfer while keeping every ego intact.

Recently I served on a jury, a fascinating experience. It was a civil, not a criminal, case. For a couple of hours we listened to the attorneys and witnesses. Then the judge gave us final instructions and we filed into the back room to deliberate.

In our county, the first person chosen automatically becomes the foreman. She took her place at the head of the table and we settled into the chairs. None of us had ever served on a jury and the foreman seemed hesitant about how to begin. Everyone hemmed and hawed. Finally, I raised my hand. (I can't help it. I'm a take-charge kind of person.)

"I have an idea," I said. "Before we have any discussion let's have each person write 'plaintiff' or 'defendant' on a slip of paper and pass it to the foreman. That way we will know how close we are to agreement. It will give us a starting point."

Secretly I was thinking, "This is a cinch. It will be 12-0. We will be the fastest jury in history."

The vote was 6-6. We all burst into laughter. It was a great ice breaker.

Secretly I was thinking, "Where were these mental midgets? Didn't they see what I saw? Didn't they hear what I heard?"

We began discussions and after an hour I called for another vote. Written. I did not want anyone to have to explain why they'd changed their mind. The vote was 7-5. (One had seen the light.) Another two hours went by and I called for a vote. It was 9-3. And there it stayed. Of the three holdouts, only one was a possible convert. In the end, the attorneys decided to abide by majority rule—something which surprised all of us. We didn't know that was an option.

As you deliberate over job or career decisions, think about that jury. We don't all see, hear, interpret, or experience things in the same way. Changing your mind about your job or career doesn't mean you were wrong. It means you are making a new decision based on new information. You are not the same person today you were yesterday. Nursing is not the same profession today it was yesterday. Everyone and everything changes. Be open to new ideas and insights. You may decide in favor of your job. You may decide against nursing. In the end your decision may be a compromise. It may be a decision that you didn't even know was an option when the whole process began.

What Next?

1. Jot down a few words describing how the following people have influenced past career decisions:

   Parents:

   Spouse:

   Children:

   Teachers:

   Boss:

   Minister/Priest/Rabbi:

   Classmates/Colleagues:

2. Describe a career decision you made just to please yourself:

3. Quitting my job would make me feel:

4. Leaving nursing would make me feel:

5. **Since I became a nurse...**

I have changed in the following ways:

____

____

____

____

____

____

Nursing has changed in the following ways:

____

____

____

____

____

____

6. List three alternatives to your current job:
   A. ____________________
   B. ____________________
   C. ____________________

7. List three alternatives to staying in nursing:
   A. ____________________
   B. ____________________
   C. ____________________

8. **Staying in my current job:**

Advantages

____

____

____

____

Disadvantages

____

____

____

____

9. **Staying in nursing:**

Advantages

____

____

____

____

Disadvantages

____

____

____

____

YOU DON'T BRING ME FLOWERS ANYMORE

The romance is gone. The relationship that once sizzled now fizzles and fades. Each takes the other for granted. No one bothers to say, "I love you." No one bothers to say much at all.

When a couple realizes their marriage is in trouble, they may try one of those marriage encounter weekends designed to enhance communication and rekindle some of the passion they originally felt. When a nurse realizes her relationship with her life's work is in trouble, it would be nice to have a career encounter weekend available to restore some of the excitement and enthusiasm she originally felt.

Think about the last time you said, "I love nursing" or "I love my job." How long has it been?

Too often the nurse takes her job for granted. Too often the hospital takes the nurse for granted. There is no love lost between them.

When nurses are in short supply, smart hospital emphasize retention rather than recruitment. They not only want you to say, "I love nursing," but "I especially love nursing at this particular hospital."

When I consult on retention strategies, I usually begin by sharing a list of six concepts which determine the level of job satisfaction and the quality of worklife for most nurses:

(1) Nurses feel significant.
(2) Learning and competence matter.
(3) Nurses are a community.
(4) Work is exciting.
(5) Nurses are pulled, not pushed, by a strong sense of mission and purpose.
(6) Quality is valued.

On the surface these concepts are deceptively simple. In the real world they are difficult to operationalize. They require a lot of thought and the commitment of time, energy, and money.

If you are unhappy with your job, look at it in light of these six concepts. What's missing? How could you help implement these ideas in your present situation? Remember, it is usually easier to *remodel* than relocate.

If you are relocating, either by choice or by chance, screen prospective employers on these six concepts. Look for evidence they are alive and well in the workplace and not just given lip service. As you read through the following examples, think about the ramifications on three levels: (1) for you as an individual professional; (2) for the hospital you currently work for or anticipate working for; and (3) for the nursing profession as a whole.

(1) NURSES FEEL SIGNIFICANT

Are the nurses called by name? There is nothing worse than feeling anonymous, like a cog in a giant machine. The principal of a large school could call every student by name. How did he do it? Flash cards. Picture of the student on one side, name on the reverse. Practice. Each student was that important to him.

Could your administrator or vice president of nursing call you by name? How many nurses can they call by name? How many nurses can you call by name?

During Nurses' Week celebrations one hospital gave each nurse 100 personalized business cards. It was one of the most popular and least expensive gestures they had ever made. A business card is evidence of mutual pride and respect between the institution and the nurse; yet few hospitals encourage or even permit their nurses to carry official business cards.

One hospital had established an "Employee of the Month" award. In eighteen months only one nurse had been chosen even though nurses accounted for 70 percent of the employees. So the nursing department established a "Nurse of the Month" award and even had each unit honoring a special nurse every month.

One head nurse had her staff bring in all their diplomas and certificates. She had them framed and hung on a prominent wall.

Morale soared. It made fascinating reading for patients, visitors, and other professionals.

(2) LEARNING AND COMPETENCE MATTER

Is there a career ladder in place that actually works? What are the opportunities for promotion and advancement?

Does your employer support education? Do they give you credit or rewards for getting additional degrees or certification? Are they willing to work with you in terms of flexible schedules or tuition reimbursement?

Elaine wanted to get her master's degree. The university program required she be available every Tuesday. She asked her supervisor to guarantee her every Tuesday off and was turned down flat. The supervisor's reasoning was, "If I do it for one, I have to do it for all." What did Elaine do? She quit. She walked right out the front door of her hospital, right into the front door of the competitor's hospital. They hired her in a flash, tickled to death to get her. Today Elaine has her master's and she still works for the competitor.

Are nurses haphazardly floated throughout the hospital? Floating reinforces the myth that nurses are interchangeable and disposable. In Saskatoon the nurses' union created a sweatshirt showing a nurse tumbling out of the bow of a boat. The poem read, "I'm a nurse, not a boat. Please don't expect me to float!"

I don't believe in floating. I do believe in crosstraining. Nurses are crosstrained in one other specialty and that is the only area to which they are pulled. This practice not only ensures nurse safety and satisfaction, but *patient* safety and satisfaction.

What is your area of specialization? What do you take pride in knowing and doing well? What other area of nursing would you like to know more about? What other skills would you like to master?

(3) NURSES ARE A COMMUNITY

Newsletters for nurses only, sports teams, social events, support groups, fitness programs, writing clubs, and community-action projects are some indications of a strong sense of community among nurses.

One nursing department "adopted" an inner city school. Some nurses served as one-on-one tutors for students in math and language skills. Others helped plan field trips, parties, and special events. Still others helped run an after-hours program for latchkey kids. The youngsters got to see nurses in a whole new light. The nurses began to see themselves in a whole new light.

A staff developer commented one day that the nurses didn't look too healthy. (Nurses are so busy taking care of others that we often neglect ourselves.) To encourage wellness she started a program called "Fun Fit." It was a simple idea based on walking your way to fitness. She went outside the hospital and marked off one-mile and two-mile paths. For days when the weather was severe, she marked off one-mile and two-mile paths right in the hospital. She sent around a sign-up sheet expecting about 40 nurses to join. Almost 400 nurses signed up! Soon they were forming teams. For example, all the nurses who worked with diabetic patients made matching T-Shirts that said 'Sugar Bears.' The program expanded to include points for aerobics, golf, tennis, swimming, etc. People in other departments asked to join. The fitness craze swept the entire hospital.

Look for evidence of nurses helping nurses. Think about your own reaction in report upon hearing there is an *old* nurse hospitalized on your unit. Ugh! No one wants to take care of an old nurse. But we are a vanishing breed, an endangered species. If we don't take care of our own, no one else will. I think we should flag the Kardex of any hospitalized nurse with a big, red sticker which means "Extra Special Red Carpet Treatment." Then we assign our best and our brightest to that nurse's care and nurses on the unit make an all-out effort to see that that nurse's needs are being met. And, in this age of few-frills-headed-for-no-frills health care, I'd like to suggest we flag the Kardex of any family member of a nurse for extra special care. There ought to be some perks in being a nurse.

A critical care nurse shared a good example of nurses helping nurses. Her younger sister had to have surgery for cancer. Her sister told her she could come and go with her through the experience but that she must come as her sister, not as a nurse. Having a family member who is a nurse hovering over the bed is difficult enough. Having a family member who is a critical care nurse hovering over the bed is the worst.

One of the staff nurses came to the door and motioned for the critical care nurse to follow her. Once outside the staff nurse said, "I just wanted to show you you're on the care plan." The critical care nurse thought it would say, "Watch it! This family member is not only a nurse but a critical care nurse!"

To her surprise they had her on the care plan as a family member who would need extra support. The staff nurse said, "Look, you are going to have to be so strong for your sister. You are going to have to be so strong for your family. You are not going to be able to look out for your own needs. If you have a problem, a question, a concern, a suggestion, bring it to us." She then took her to the nurses' lounge area and said, "If you need to get away from family for a few minutes, just to sort things out or take a breather, you're welcome in here anytime. You're a colleague."

A few years ago I met a bunch of operating room nurses who were having a problem with some surgeons who had taken up nurse bashing as kind of a hobby. They loved to scream, yell, belittle, and generally harass nurses.

You know what usually happens when a fellow nurse is being royally chewed out; it is embarrassing. Most of us duck around the corner. We stay out of sight pretending we didn't hear or see anything.

These OR nurses decided to take a different approach. Whenever a nurse was being harassed, you would hear over the intercom, "CODE 13 -- Nurse's Station." Every available nurse would drop what she was doing, rush to the spot, and stand right behind the nurse being hassled. It was so intimidating. The doctors would fall silent and back away. It took them one week to change behavior. You know how behavior modification works.

If worked so well they decided to keep it and, whenever a nurse needed nurse-to-nurse backup for whatever reason, she could call a CODE 13. It worked so well in the OR, it spread throughout the hospital. Wouldn't it be nice to know that if you got into difficulty, you could pick up the phone and say, "Room 2l2, CODE 13," and every nurse in your cafeteria would rise to her feet and rally to your support?

At Baptist Hospital of Miami they have CODE PINK, as opposed to CODE BLUE. Their approach is a little different in that they circle the offending physician. They form a ring right around him.

The first time it happened the doctor came unglued. He looked around, found the most petite nurse in the circle, and broke through. He immediately went to the Vice President of Nursing, a dynamo named Charlotte Dison, and demanded to know what was going on. She calmly replied it was their new policy. Anyone who got out of control would be circled. He laughed and said, "Then you don't have to worry about me. I'm not going through that again!" He changed his behavior.

Not long ago I had a message on my answering machine that said, "I'm interested in CODE PINK or CODE 13 but I can find no reference to it in the literature."

As I dialed her number I was thinking, "Nurses are such gutless wonders. We can't do anything spontaneously. We have to have chapter and verse for everything." Then I thought, "Perhaps this is a student. Perhaps she's writing a paper and her instructor won't accept it without proper documentation."

The caller turned out to be with a hospital in Florida. I told her I was the one spreading rumors about CODE 13 but that CODE PINK was right there in her state. I suggested she talk with Charlotte Dison. Or, I suggested, she could call Helen Cox, Associate Dean, at Texas Tech University. She is doing research on verbal abuse and calculates about 18 percent of nurses who leave our profession attribute it to verbal harassment and verbal abuse.

As I continued to give suggestions, she interrupted me saying, "It's not like we're *not* going to do it. We're *going* to do it. We are calling it CODE PINK and we're ready. Our nurse managers are standing by. When they hear CODE PINK called, they are going to go and back that nurse up. Our VP of Nursing is standing by. When she hears the code, she is going to go and back that nurse up. Our problem ***is*** the doctors aren't misbehaving."

I burst into laughter.

She continued, "We think they've gotten wind of this. We think they know what is going to happen."

Still laughing I said, "It doesn't matter. It really doesn't matter. Because either way you've won. You have done what you set out to do. But let me tell you what I think has happened. Because your nurses know they will be supported all the way up the chain of command clear through the Vice President for Nursing, your nurses are walking differently and talking differently. And the doctors sense the difference."

You and I have both worked with nurses who are victimized all the time. Their body language says, "Take me, use me, kick me, walk on me." And we've both worked with nurses who have a gleam in their eye that says, "Mess with me and die." Nobody jerks those nurses around.

Finding support for nurses and nursing all the way up the chain of command means this is a great place to work.

(4) WORK IS EXCITING

When was the last time you got up in the morning and looked forward to going to work? Work occupies such a significant part of our lives, it should be more than tolerable. It should be pleasurable.

Sometimes the silliest things can make a big difference. Like the nurse who posted a big sign that said "THINK PINK" and claimed it was National Think Pink Week. Before long, even colleagues who were suffering from a severe case of the midwinter blahs got into the spirit. Pink balloons, pink pencils, pink memos, pink cookies, pink flowers began appearing. By the end of the week, nurses were wearing pink shoelaces and the doctors were wearing pink ties.

Having secret pals or birthday clubs or contests can make work more fun. A day surgery unit sponsors events like Crazy Sox Day and Ugly Earring Day. They found it not only boosted nurses' morale but entertained patients as well.

Just before Valentine's day a head nurse noticed some frilly paper doilies at the grocery store. She hadn't thought about those for years. She bought a couple of packages and then cut out red construction paper hearts. She glued a heart in the middle of each doily. The next morning she pinned one on every nurse on her unit. Suddenly everyone in the hospital wanted one. People came from every department and floor asking if they could have one pinned on them. She spent the rest of the day cutting, pasting, and pinning decorations on people. Little things mean a lot.

One Vice President of Nursing asked each head nurse to choose the most creative nurse on her staff. The creative nurses were brought together and asked to brainstorm how things might be done better. They came up with almost a hundred ideas. A half dozen task forces were formed and implementation began.

One head nurse, concerned about morale and a climbing turnover rate, instituted a N.U.T.S. group which stood for Nurses Under Too Much Stress. He began with a social hour every Friday evening at the local pub. It expanded into other social events. Morale improved and turnover stopped.

Allow nurses to try out a new specialty area. Encourage nurses to get involved in research or to experiment with a pet project of their own. Form a speakers bureau. Loan nurses as consultants to other agencies. All help to make work more exciting and more satisfying.

The idea of shared governance, where nurses are actively involved in decision-making and policy-setting, gets a lot of press but not much practice. If you want to see it fully operational, visit St. Joseph's of Atlanta. They have been working on it for more than a decade and nobody does it better. Their nurses actually compete for the privilege of serving on councils which determine everything from nursing practice to education to image.

When I presented a program there, my hostess was wearing a very striking ruby pin. I assumed it was a school pin. After seeing ruby pins on several nurses, I assumed it was a survivor pin —ten years of service or something like that. Finally I asked and was told it was their C.A.P. pin (Clinical Advisor Program). The ones with the ruby pins had completed a preceptor program. St. Joseph's had found their highest turnover was among new grads and nurses who had returned to their careers after a long absence. To cut turnover, they established the C.A.P. program and it has been phenomenally successful.

The pin acts rather like the block parent sign. You know, the picture of the hand in the window which tells children this is a safe house to go to in time of trouble. If I need information, guidance, or support, I can go to a person with a ruby pin and they will help me in a confidential manner.

Serving as a preceptor makes work exciting. Good hospitals carefully prepare people for this role. Great hospitals appropriately reward them.

(5) NURSES ARE PULLED, NOT PUSHED, BY A STRONG SENSE OF MISSION AND PURPOSE

Nursing has intangible, intrinsic rewards that cannot be matched in many other occupations. Nurses do important work. Sometimes when we are tired and cranky, we forget that. We need to remind ourselves and each other of our purpose. Nursing is not just a way to make a living; it is a way of life.

Your sense of mission and purpose must be shared by the organization. Look for evidence that the hospital's philosophy is not just a dust-gathering document which no one reads, let alone lives. Look for actions, not words. Many preach kindness, compassion, and self-sacrifice but practice a ruthless, anything-for-a-buck management style.

Organizations with a strong sense of mission and purpose pull their people along. They are into leadership instead of coercion and control. Everyone is caught up in the enthusiasm and spirit of adventure. There is the sense of marching toward a grand common goal instead of stumbling along trying to avoid disaster.

One year the American Organization of Nurse Executives sponsored a contest called "My Nurse Made a Difference" in which patients or their families were encouraged to write essays about the impact a nurse had on their lives. Although AONE only conducted the contest once, their idea was picked up by several state nursing associations and hospitals throughout the country. It is a wonderful idea. Could you help sponsor such a contest on your unit or in your hospital?

Sometimes we also need to be reminded of how much impact patients have on our lives. Try this experiment. Close your eyes. Picture your most unforgettable patient. It's difficult to do. Not because you can't think of one but because you can think of so many.

A bunch of nurses was having what Sandy Crandall of the Center for Nursing Excellence would call a WHINE & JEESE PARTY. You know: "Whine" I ever become a nurse, "jeese" I hate this job. To get them out of their self-pitying mood, one nurse suggested they make a list of all the people they would never have met if they hadn't chosen nursing. As the list grew, an amazing change came over the group. They began to remember why they had come into nursing in the first place and why they had stayed in spite of some of the drawbacks.

One of the things people in any line of work crave most is "meaningful work." Nursing has that in spades.

Not long ago I did a program for a group of palliative care nurses in Canada. There were fifteen nurses, each assigned to a different hospital. They wanted to do some creative problem solving, and topping the list of problems was their feeling of being isolated and alone in their work. They often felt their role was misunderstood and they seemed to fall between the cracks—neither staff nor management. I was assured they all knew each other and didn't need name tags. However, since I didn't know them, I asked each nurse around the table to share her name, hospital, and how she had become interested in palliative care.

Each story was different. Each was inspiring. You could feel the pride growing in that group. Knowing a peron's name does not mean you know them.

There are over two million nurses in the United States and each one has a story to tell that would make us all proud.

(6) QUALITY IS VALUED

The caliber of care at any institution is directly correlated with the caliber of nurse it employs. Go with the winners. Go where your colleagues will make you proud. Any institution can claim quality. Look for evidence of commitment to quality.

Susan, an enterostomal therapy nurse, was carrying a horrendous patient load. She and another nurse were trying to serve over 1200 patients. A third nurse had long been promised but had not been delivered.

One day she approached the administrator about getting time and money to attend a three-day conference to improve her skills. She told him if they were to continue to provide excellent care, this course was essential. He looked her in the eye and said slowly, "We don't need excellent. We need adequate."

It was like a slap in the face. At that instant she knew there would be no third nurse. She thanked him for being candid. Then she took vacation time, paid her own way to the conference, and posted her name on the job-search board. When I met her she was busily sorting through offers, looking for a place where quality was indeed valued.

A recently appointed director of nursing wanted to find a way to say "thanks" to her nursing staff at Christmas time. She looked through a catalog and found a pen on a rope inscribed with "Thank You" for $1.39 each. When she approached the administrator with the idea, his response was, "Lord, that would cost us nearly $1000!" She felt so strongly about this that she actually paid for the pens herself. The nurses loved the pens. Her small act of kindness had spinoff value she never envisioned. It gave every nurse on the staff a reason to speak to her. We've all been brought up to say thank you for gifts. A nurse would approach her to say ""Thanks for the pen," and then continue to chat about ideas, problems, new programs, special events, hopes, fears, dreams.

A nurse executive was told she needed to dilute her nursing staff with ancillary help. She was told she had too rich a mix. Before agreeing to do that she required the CEO and Chairman of the Board to follow a nurse for a day. She opened the invitation up to the rest of the Board and a half dozen accepted. You can imagine she chose her nurses very carefully—top-notch, extraordinary nurses. Then she told them that while they had the administrator or board member in tow they were not to do anything unusual. All she wanted them to do was "think aloud" so the person with them would know what was going on in their minds. The experience was so impressive, the request to dilute the Registered Nurse staff was withdrawn.

As part of the Nurses' Week celebrations, another Vice President for Nursing decided to invite other department heads and VIPs to "shadow" a nurse so they could learn what nurses really do. They could choose to accompany a nurse from 7-11 a.m. or 3-7 p.m. She sent out 40 invitations How many do you think accepted?

Well, if you are like most nurses, you'll guess two or three. Shame on us! Sixty people went. Of the original forty, only one doctor defaulted and he was the first one signed up the following year. She received calls from others in the hospital, from community and business leaders, from journalists, from high school seniors all hoping to shadow a nurse.

Participants were amazed at what nurses do on a day-to-day, moment-by-moment basis. Even those you would assume already knew what nurses do, like the CEO and members of the board, were surprised by how much they learned. They simply had no idea of the split-second decision making and critical problem solving that fall to the nurse. They began to understand what quality care is all about.

Whether shopping for a new job or trying to revitalize your old job, keep these six concepts in mind. They make the difference between a job that is good and a job that is great.

What Next?

1. Describe a situation in which you really loved being a nurse:

2. The next time you are with a group of nurses, ask them to write out a situation in which they really loved being a nurse. Call for five minutes of total silence—no giggling, whispering, sneezing, or slurping— and set a timer. Then ask for volunteers to share what they have written.

3. Discuss the six concepts to increase job satisfaction and improve the quality of work life with your colleagues:

Nurses feel significant.

Learning and competence matter.

Nurses are a community.

Work is exciting.

Nurses are pulled, not pushed, by a strong sense of mission and purpose.

Quality is valued.

Take each one and make a list of how it is being operationalized today in your organization. Then list new ways you might try implementing those concepts tomorrow.

THE HONEYMOON IS OVER

First jobs are like first loves. The experience may be passionate but it is rarely permanent. That's why employers are often reluctant to hire new graduates. They know new grads are fragile and fickle. Fragile in that they need more support, guidance, time, and attention. Fickle in that they are full of romantic notions and will play the field, looking for the ideal job. When the going gets tough, they get gone. They head down the road, looking for greener pastures.

If you feel fragile and fickle, you are not alone. New graduates are under a lot of pressure. While you were in school, there was always an escape clause. You could change your mind and your major. Now you have graduated. Like getting married, graduating has a ring of finality about it. You are not *going* to be a nurse, you are one!

Graduation often brings elation followed quickly by depression. Not unusual—great achievement is often followed by a let down. Your life has been so tightly structured, so highly goal-directed, you had no time to breathe. Until you can establish new patterns and set new goals, there is a void. Post-graduation blues are common, normal, and temporary. So relax.

Unfortunately, school did not prepare you for work anymore than courtship prepared you for marriage. Living with nursing day in and out, up close and personal, is different than visiting it three times a week. The honeymoon is over. The daily grind begins. The first year in any marriage or career is tough.

Getting a job is the next hurdle. For some of you, making that first job decision is a done deal. You will be living and working in the same community where you went to school. Opportunities are specific and limited. Glamorous assignments in far away places may call but you cannot answer. Your life is here.

Be realistic. Don't torture yourself.

Get an area map and mark off hospitals within a certain number of miles or minutes. If you are in a major metropolitan area, you may have twenty hospitals from which to choose. If you are in a small town, you may have only one.

If you are footloose and fancy free, you will have more trouble making a decision. In a nurse shortage, jobs are plentiful everywhere. Pick the city of your choice. Before setting off to see the world, however, you may want to get a year of experience under your belt. It will be less stressful than tackling to a new job, a new career, and a new community simultaneously.

In either case, the best way to approach this difficult decision is to take a piece of paper and split it into four quadrants. Label one half Job A: Advantages and Disadvantages, the other half Job B: Advantages and Disadvantages. Fill in each section as best you can; then go in search of more information. Visit the facility, interview staff nurses, talk with last year's graduates, contact faculty for recommendations, eavesdrop in the cafeteria, see the nurse recruiter.

In any given community, nursing salaries will be virtually the same. Only a few pennies per hour will separate one from another. Beware of any hospital offering bonuses or unusually high salaries by local standards. There is always a reason why they offer combat pay.

In fact, salary should be one of your last considerations in choosing a first job. You need to go where you can learn real-world nursing. You want to go where they provide an adequate orientation, a modified internship, access to mentors and preceptors, and nurse support groups.

Also consider which institutions offer perks important to you. Each nurse has different needs and desires. What do you want most? Dental care, on-site child care, tuition reimbursement, opportunities to specialize, an easy commute?

Narrow your selection down by playing one institution off against another. Take the winner and compare it with the next challenger. If you get to a point where you are torn between two seemingly equal opportunities, break the tie by flipping a coin, Flip a coin? Yes. Let me explain.

Every nurse has come to a personal or professional crossroads and stood immobilized, terrified of making the wrong choice, the wrong decision. I've been there too, and the most helpful piece of advice I can offer comes from Theodore Isaac Rubin's book: **Overcoming Indecisiveness**.

Rubin says the big fact is: in very few situations does it actually make any difference which decision you make. (Whew! Is that a relief!) It doesn't matter whether you move to New York or stay in Iowa, take the job in Med-Surg or in Psych, marry Fred or Charlie. You can be successful either way. Because success is not determined by *which* decision you make; it is determined by the level of commitment once the decision is made.

Rubin says very few people have the ability to pull out all stops, to commit wholeheartedly, to back their decisions to the hilt, 110 percent. If you can do that, you can make a success of almost anything.

If your experience is like mine, I have not yet faced a decision that did not have strong advantages and strong disadvantages on both sides. I think that lends credibility to Rubin's theory that you can be successful either way. Commitment will determine success.

When I suggested you flip a coin to break the deadlock between two jobs, I was not joking. It works. Every year I teach dozens of workshops with a decision-making focus. In one such workshop a nurse was trying to decide whether to stay in Denver or move to Seattle. After painstakingly identifying all the pros and cons, Jeanne was even more frustrated. She couldn't decide. I told her to bring me a quarter and I would tell her exactly what she should do.

As the two of us stood in front of 200 other nurses, I told her I was going to flip the coin. Heads she moved to Seattle. Tails she stayed in Denver. There was complete silence as the coin flip-flopped through the air. When it came up heads I said, "Congratulations! You are moving to Seattle!!! How do you feel about that?" With barely a moment's hesitation, she shot back, "I'm so excited! I can hardly wait to get going!"

The audience burst into laughter. Of course, she didn't have to live by the flip of the coin. What was obvious to everyone, including Jeanne, was that she could commit wholeheartedly. She could make a success of the move. In her heart-of-hearts she wanted to go.

If the color had drained from her face upon hearing "heads" or if she had physically backed away from me, sputtering a list of reasons why she shouldn't or couldn't move, we would have known that even if coerced into a move, she would sabotage herself. The move would be extremely stressful and probably not successful.

In another workshop I was dealing with nurse managers. Ruthann was struggling with whether to keep her job (she had a very good job) or open her own business. I told her to bring me a quarter. The coin toss said she should stay in her job. Before I could even get that complete sentence out of my mouth, her face fell. Her whole body slumped. She was **so** disappointed.

Time out for a reality check. Again, Ruthann did not have to live by the flip of a coin. What was obvious to everyone in the room was that she had already emotionally disengaged from her job. She was primed and ready to make a change.

If she did not follow her gut-level instincts, she would probably always regret it. The unhappiest people in life are not the ones who saw opportunity, went out on a limb, and failed. They are the ones who saw opportunity and lacked the courage to go out on the limb after it. They continue to kick themselves 20, 30, 40 years after the fact.

Once you decide on which job to take, commit completely—body, mind, and spirit. It is the key to success.

Enter the new job as you would a new class. This is where real learning begins. Some employers and colleagues will expect you to be fully functional five minutes after graduation. You and I know that just does not happen. While you have the basic knowledge you need, you lack street smarts. You are about to learn all the things they never taught you in nursing school. Welcome to Working Nurse 101!

The transition from student to practitioner is rigorous, so take special care of yourself. Keep your life as uncomplicated as possible. Make sure to get enough rest, eat right, and exercise.

Cut yourself some slack even when others don't. Instead of agonizing over what went wrong each day, take a moment and write down one or two of the good things that happened while you were on duty. Keep a diary. Track your progress. After three months, six months, a year, you will be much more comfortable as a nurse. Have fun. Take up a sport or hobby. Reactivate your social life. Go where you want to go; do what you want to do. There is so much more to life than your job.

Keep things light. One unit experienced a horrendous turnover. If was staffed almost entirely by new graduates. The head nurse helplessly watched them struggle. Morale was so low she thought they would not only leave her unit, but leave nursing.

During a particularly tense moment, as one new grad passed by a stricken colleague, she sang softly, "Don't Worry, Be Happy." That popular song became their secret rallying cry. Within 30 days, things had completely turned around. All the new grads made it. They didn't lose a one. Today that head nurse boasts she has the best staff in the hospital.

So...take your fragile, fickle, new graduate self and find the best possible job you can. Commit completely, Pamper yourself during these next few months. Keep your sense of humor. Stick together with your colleagues and "Don't Worry, Be Happy."

What Next?

1. Let's go shopping! Even if you are not a senior student or a new graduate, pretend you are in the market for a job.
   A. Read and clip out advertisements of nursing jobs (local and national) that appeal to you. Keep them in a shoebox or a notebook. What do the ads have in common?
   B. Decide how far you are willing to commute. How many minutes a day are you willing to spend on the road going to and from work.
   C. Take a local map. Make circles from your home which would correspond with 15, 30, 45, and 60 minute drives.
   D. Now make a list of all facilities within those circles that employ nurses: hospitals, clinics, schools, doctors' offices, health departments, insurance agencies.
   E. Call and inquire about employment opportunities.
   F. Other than salary, what would the six most appealing fringe benefits be to you:
      (1)
      (2)
      (3)
      (4)
      (5)
      (6)

2. Re-examine the last major decision in your life—choosing a school, buying a car, having a baby, moving. Describe the steps you took, who you turned to for advice, how pleased you are with the outcome.
3. When you next major decision comes along, use this format:

CHOICE A	CHOICE B
ADVANTAGES	ADVANTAGES
DISADVANTAGES	DISADVANTAGES

4. Try the coin flip.

5. List three ways you are going to take better care of yourself:

On Duty	Off Duty
(1)	(1)
(2)	(2)
(3)	(3)

SALLY BROWN
FOR
GOVERNOR
SALLY'S
THE
ONE

SOMETHING OLD, SOMETHING NEW, SOMETHING BORROWED, SOMETHING BLUE

For nine long years I was exiled to the deserts of Eastern Washington State. I lived on the edge of the Hanford Atomic Reservation in the nevergreen part of the Evergreen State, an area that is hot, dusty, isolated, ugly, and boring. My husband took me there under false pretenses. He said we'd be there for two years and then move on to Seattle or Portland. Men! They promise you anything and then don't deliver. We were there nine long years.

And for nine long years I whined.

When the Department of Energy offered Gary a transfer to the Washington, DC, area, I was ecstatic. I had been begging to return to civilization. I wanted to go to a city—any city.

In February, Gary left to begin his new assignment. He left me with two teenage sons, a dog, four vehicles, and a house to be packed, moved, sold, or otherwise disposed of, not necessarily in that order. I was also facing the most ambitious lecture schedule of my life. As I crisscrossed the country, racking up the frequent flyer miles, I was racked with guilt. Half the time our sons could not answer the question, "Kids, do you know where your parents are tonight?"

Seven months later, exasperated and exhausted, I arrived at our new home bringing with me the kids, the dog, and two vehicles. The moving van, bulging with ten tons of irreplaceable stuff, was only hours behind me. By sundown the house was bulging. Before the dust settled, I began my fall lecture schedule. I never had time to catch my breath.

When I first knew I would be moving to the DC area, I contacted Denise Cavanaugh. We had met a few years earlier in Toronto. A college had brought us together to conduct a management seminar. When I arrived at the hotel, Denise invited me to dinner. We sat and talked for hours. I was floundering, struggling with decisions about my professional life, starving for advice and direction. Denise was not a nurse, but a business woman with a very successful consulting firm in Washington, DC. She was the first person to share openly about her own experience: how she had gotten started, how she set fees, how she found clients, how she handled some of the nitty-gritty problems that were tormenting me.

When I told Denise I would be moving to her "neighborhood," she immediately invited me to meet the other two principals in her company: Ann Hagan and Jane Pierson. Their firm was interested in venturing farther into health care. I was interested in venturing out. It was a whole new world for me. I was awed. Not only did I suddenly have access to the nation's capital, I had access to professional colleagues of the first order.

We held a couple of meetings to discuss possibilities. It was invigorating and exciting. I really expected Cavanaugh, Hagan, and Pierson, Inc., to make a proposal. We seemed to be a good match.

September, October, November disappeared in a frenzy of activity. I was on the road nonstop. Paperwork, unpacking and re-packing took up the few days I had at home. Chaos reigned in my personal and professional life.

When I finished my last workshop December 12th, I was exhausted. I dreaded the holidays. When we drove by the tree lots I would mumble, "I suppose we should get a tree." (I had no idea where our ornaments were.) Finally I asked the boys, "What would you think if we didn't have a tree this year?" They quickly replied, "That's okay—as long as we have **presents**!" It was like, "Come on, Mom, get your priorities straight!"

So, for the first year in my entire life, there was no Christmas tree.

December 15th I had lunch with Denise. She turned the tables on me. She asked **me** to write a proposal to their firm. I stuttered and stammered. I told her I would try but that something was wrong. It was like my brain had short circuited. I couldn't seem to concentrate or make decisions. Denise reassured me it didn't have to be anything formal, just a starting point for further discussions.

Walking to the Metro Station, I felt numb. I didn't need this. I needed someone else to take charge, someone else to think things through, someone else to make decisions, someone else to do the work. But the ball was back in my court.

Then a happy thought struck me. My sister, Sue, was coming to visit the first week in January. I would get Sue to write the proposal! After all, she was a businesswoman. Her brains worked.

When Sue arrived I described the situation and told her I needed to make a proposal. She began to ask questions: How did Pro-Nurse fit in with Cavanaugh, Hagan, and Pierson? What were my expectations? Their expectations? What were my goals? Where did I want the business to be in five years, in ten years?

I interrupted her. "Sue, don't tell me this stuff. ***I teach this stuff!*** I am trying to tell you. Something is wrong. My brain is on the fritz. I'm like one of the pod people. The body snatchers must have sucked out all my gray matter."

She *wouldn't* write the proposal. I *couldn't* write the proposal. So instead we did all the great tourist things I hadn't had time to do and then she flew home.

Denise called. "How is the proposal coming?"

I said, "Wednesday, 2 p.m."

For the next couple of days I walked around the house with two pieces of paper in my pocket. One titled "What I Want" and the other titled "What I am Willing to do to Get it."

Forced to confront the problem by a deadline of my own making, I struggled with all those questions I'd been avoiding. What did I really want? Did I want to dissolve Pro-Nurse? Did I want to become part of their firm? What could I offer them? What could they offer me? Where did I want to be in two years?

Five years? Ten years?

Slowly the fog began to lift. More accurately, my depression began to lift. I had been in a full-blown clinical depression but I didn't recognize it in myself. (And I'm supposed to be a psych nurse!)

One of my favorite workshops I call Walk-on-Water Women. (WOW for short.) It's about the risks, rewards, and realities of being a high achiever. It's about trying to do it all, have it all, and be it all. I not only teach this workshop, I live it . Out of the blue (no pun intended) it struck me that I had been depressed.

I have a list of eight signs and symptoms of depression from the American Psychiatric Association. If you have four of the symptoms for two weeks, you are clinically depressed. I looked at that list and exclaimed, "Egad! I have six out of the eight signs of depression!" The only two I didn't have were that I was not suicidal and I was not losing weight. I had all the others:

Feelings of worthlessness and guilt—YUP!

Fatigue—double YUP!

Sleep disturbances—does being up at 2 or 3 a.m. banging away on the computer count?—YUP!

Changes in psychomotor activity —YUP!

Inability to think or concentrate—uhhhhh...?

Loss of libido—Well, I'm not sure I lost it but I certainly didn't know what to do with it. Most of the time Gary and I weren't even in the same city, much less the same bed.

"Depleted." That's a more descriptive word than depressed for what had happpened to me. I had been running on empty for a long time. During those few weeks in December and January I had started to replenish my reserves. Having just a bit of rest and recreation had worked wonders.

Even as I wrestled with that proposal, I could feel my batteries recharging. Things began to crystallize. I realized I did not want to disband Pro-Nurse. The fatigue and isolation had temporarily weakened me. My vision had blurred but not vanished.

When I met with Denise on Wednesday I had three sheets of paper titled:

What I Want ...
What I Am Willing and Able To Do...
Possibilities...

Each contained a scant outline, a hundred words at most. What I **wanted** included continuing Pro-Nurse, acquiring a Washington DC address, having access to colleagues (I'd felt isolated and alone for so long), getting more experience as a consultant, not just a speaker, possible political involvement, editorial/publishing experience (I had enough writing experience), and public relations/marketing experience.

What I was **willing and able to do** included serving as their in-house editor and helping them develop their speakers' bureau in exchange for things like office space, secretarial backup, and a chance to observe and learn from them.

Possibilities included a variety of ways the above might be implemented.

Those scraps of paper contained my strategic plan. Even though I didn't know how or when or if all those elements would ever come into being, I suddenly had a new sense of mission, purpose, and direction. I knew where I wanted to go. And, it's been my experience that once you know where you want to go, you begin to consciously and unconsciously map out ways to get there.

Do you know where you want to go? Do you have a strategic plan? Few nurses do. They don't know where they want to go. They only know that where they are is not where they want to be.

Actually strategic planning is something more likely to be undertaken by a large corporation than a lone individual. Usually the Grand High Muckty Mucks of the organization go on a retreat where they contemplate their corporate navel, considering business past, present, and future. They re-examine, redefine, and re-commit.

A strategic plan is the destination, the ultimate goal, the best possible scenario. It requires visionary and heroic thinking. The strategic plan ensures consistency, determines decisions, guides actions, inspires confidence, generates support and sustains commitment.

When an organization forms a strategic plan, the first two questions are:

Where are we?

Where do we want to go?

When I challenge a seminar group to come up with a strategic plan for nursing, I ask them to travel into the future 10 or 20 years. What do they envision for nursing? What would the ideal be? This is what they see: Nursing as a full-fledged profession and nurses as powerful people.

NURSING AS A FULL-FLEDGED PROFESSION

Respected
Sought after
Reimbursed
Organized
Politically connected
Highly visible
Research driven
Redefining health
Controlling health care

NURSES AS POWERFUL PEOPLE

Professional
Articulate
Well-educated
Affluent
Accountable
Respected
Highly specialized
Proud
Active in professional organizations
Politically astute
Establishing health care policy
Independent practitioners
Owning, operating, and controlling health care facilities
Strong camaraderie and cohesiveness among nurses

Their lists answer the second question: Where do we want to go? Their lists also speak volumes about the first question: Where are we?

Today's nurse feels less than professional and less than powerful. Therein lies the rub. It explains much of the unrest and attrition we are experiencing.

The third question to ask in strategic planning is:

Can we get there from here?

There needs to be some evaluation of how realistic and attainable these goals are. There also needs to be an ETA— an estimated time of arrival.

The last questions to be answered are crucial:

What decisions must be made?
What actions must be taken?

For example, if the strategic plan calls for making nursing a full-fledged profession, then the decision about how to educate future nurses is automatically made. The baccalaureate degree would be the bare minimum. Graduate school would be the norm.

This is a fundamental decision that nursing has been unwilling or unable to make. I graduated from a diploma program in 1963 and was told I would need my bachelor's degree. Silly me, I believed them and continued my education. Over a third of a century later, we are still torn apart by our indecision and inaction on this issue. One of my favorite quotations is from Edna St. Vincent Millay. She said, "Life is not one damn thing after another. It's the same damn thing over and over."

If nursing's strategic plan is to be an occupation, then we could continue to educate at any and all levels. However, if our strategic plan is to be a profession, we are going to have to bite the bullet. We are going to have to convert and play by rules of the planet. Rules that you and I did not make and may not like, but nursing is not the exception.

Can it be that simple? Just one decision: occupation or profession? Then action.

One university has a staggeringly high failure rate on State Board Exams. They are committed to accepting educationally disadvantaged students. Their mission is to take high-risk students and make nurses out of them. Given their strategic plan, they argue, their failure rate is acceptable.

Their mission is noble. That does not make it smart.

"You don't build a business. You build people. And people build the business." That's a quote more or less from Zig Ziglar. I would like to bend it a bit and make it read, "You don't build nursing. You build nurses. And nurses build nursing."

You and I are the individual building blocks of nursing. If we continue to create a less than professional nurse, we will continue to have less than a profession. The two cannot be separated.

Let's remove this discussion from the global aspects and bring it back down to the individual level. I have two master's degrees but I am no longer able to teach at the university level. Some days that really gets my goat. I am a good teacher and I love to work with students. But nursing wants to be accepted on the college or university campus by all other disciplines and that requires faculty to be educated at the doctoral level. I do not like that in my personal life but I support it philosophically because that is the direction I want to see nursing move. So I have two choices. I can go back to school and get my Ph.D. or I can make other career plans.

As you can see from my strategic plan, I made other career decisions. There is nothing in it about continuing my education or securing a faculty position.

"Creating My Future" is the title of one of my workshop handouts. Just saying that phrase aloud initiates hope and a new sense of power. It helps make the transition from being reaction-oriented to action-oriented.

At the top is a space for the strategic plan. Underneath are columns for short-term and long-term goals which will make that plan a reality. Underneath the goals are daily priorities. It is the day-to-day actions which feed the goals which in turn bring about the strategic plan—the ultimate goal. There is often a total disconnect between the three layers. The organization or the individual gives the strategic plan lip service but fails to establish priorities or carry out goals that would actually lead to the desired destination.

What Next?

It's time to do a little strategic planning of your own. You are the Grand High Muckety Muck of your life. It's time for you to contemplate your business past, present, and future. It's time for you to re-examine, re-define, and re-commit.

SOMETHING OLD:

There are times when it is helpful to look back. Think about your past jobs and all the twists and turns in your career. Take pride in your past accomplishments. Relish them. A clue to your future may be hidden there. Think about your failures and disappointments. What have you learned from them? What has being a nurse meant to you? What elements of nursing have brought you the most pleasure and the most pain?

What I've enjoyed most about nursing is:

What I've liked least about nursing is:

SOMETHING NEW:

Take a look ahead. Where would you like to go, whom would you like to meet, what would you like to learn? What would the best possible scenario be for you? What is your mission, purpose, direction? **Write your strategic plan down and study it.** *Caution: The moment you begin to write out your plan, a little voice within will start to sabotage you. Ignore that voice and the doubts it will try to instill. Write out a grand, glorious, heroic strategic plan, even if you think there is no way you could possibly get there from here.*

SOMETHING BORROWED:

Take the questions a huge corporation would ask and apply them to yourself:

1. Where am I?
2. Where do I want to go?
3. Can I get there from here?
4. What is my estimated time of arrival?
5. What decisions must I make?
6. What actions must I take?

Follow the example of corporate planners. Go on a retreat. It may just involve checking into a local hotel for 24 or 48 hours. Get away from the normal hassles and distractions. Take your brains, a pencil and paper, and get cracking. Someone has observed we spend more time planning our vacations than we spend planning our lives.

SOMETHING BLUE:

This is not an exercise to be done when you are "blue"—depressed, exhausted, exasperated, depleted. And the strategic plan is not something that will happen "out of the blue." This is not magic. This is work.

Finally, remember the strategic plan is not carved in stone. On the way to your destination, you may bump into new opportunities or surprising options. Stay alert. Stay flexible. As President Eisenhower said, "Plans are worthless. Planning is essential."

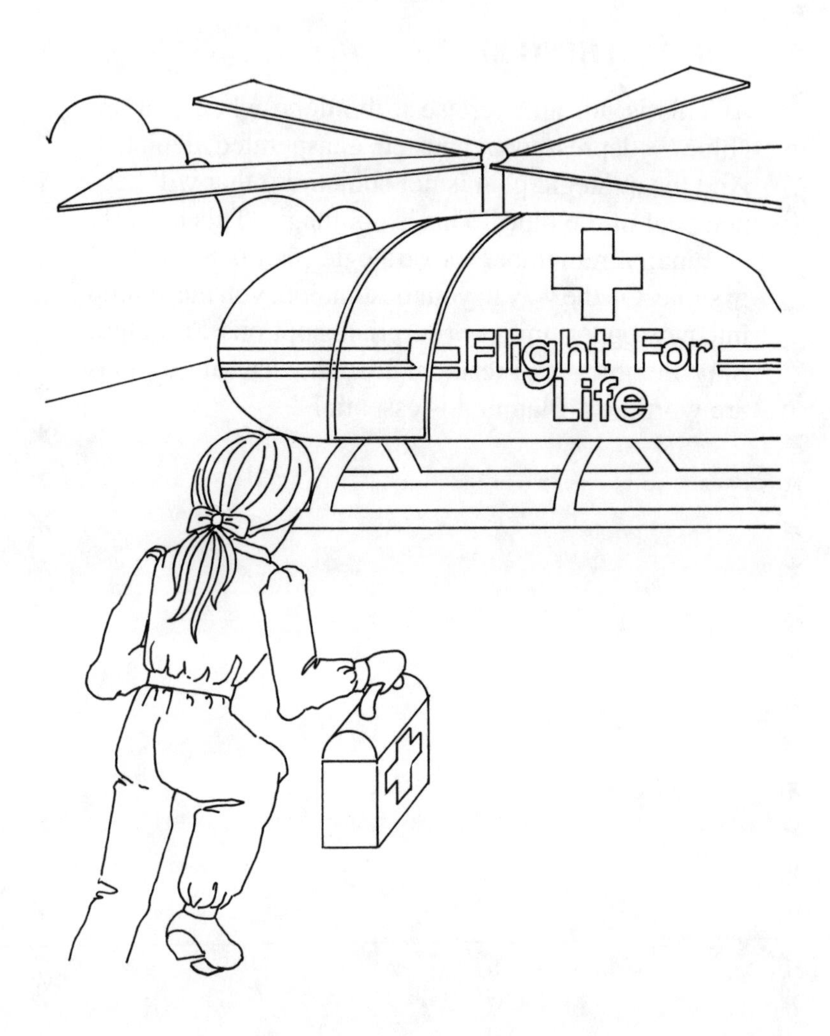
Flight For
Life

SETTLING DOWN

Admit it. Didn't you feel just a touch of glee watching Donald Trump topple?

"The bigger they are the harder they fall."

That's why so many of us hug the ground. We are afraid of falling.

There's a theory known as "life equation" which suggests if you think your life should add up to 10, you will surround yourself with people, places, activities, and decisions which ensure that you do not exceed 10. However, if you think your life should add up to 100, you will surround yourself with much higher caliber people, places, activities, and decisions. It is directly correlated with self-esteem.

A "ground-hugger" reading this will ask, "But what if you think your life should add up to 100 and you only make it to 47? Think how disappointed you would be!"

You tell me. On a scale of 1-100, would you rather live your life as a 10 or a 47? Yes, Donald Trump fell and fell hard. But financially he still landed miles above you and me.

When I graduated from high school, smart young women were directed toward the teaching and nursing professions. Of course, there were women in other occupations but it was rare and it was risky for women to venture into careers not approved for female use. So we "settled down" and made the best of the situation.

Today's smart young women have a myriad of choices, yet the vast majority cluster in very traditional, female-dominated occupations. Women continue to settle down.

"Better safe than sorry."

Perhaps you once dreamed of being something else—a veterinarian, architect, couturier, musician, journalist, engineer, interpreter, scientist, actress, explorer. When you shared your dreams, you were told, "Be practical!"

So you settled down. You chose nursing because it was safe, secure, and socially acceptable. Now you can't stop the nagging feeling you could have been something else. Something more.

Perhaps you didn't even choose nursing. As one nurse wrote, "My father chose nursing for me. He refused to pay my tuition for any other course of study. At seventeen, with no other means of support and little self-esteem, I bowed to his wishes. I still get angry every time I think about it."

There are a lot of angry nurses. There are a lot of depressed nurses. You hear it when they talk. The angry nurses bitch and the depressed nurses whine. When nurses get together, the tone and content of their conversation is often negative.

Psychologists speak of mind chatter. Evidently just below the level of consciousness, we continually babble to ourselves. When the content of such subconscious chatter is explored, 75 percent is found to be negative. Nurse chatter. Maybe there is a correlation.

The mind can be re-programmed by using affirmations to counteract the negative subtalk:

NEGATIVE SUBTALK	CONSCIOUS AFFIRMATIONS
I'm always late.	I'm punctual.
I'm not very coordinated.	I'm skillful.
I'm lazy.	I'm ambitious.
I'll never amount to much.	I'm successful.
I never remember names	I have an excellent memory.
Dime a dozen.	Unique.
Stupid, stupid, stupid . . .	Smart, smart, smart . . .

Actually for something presumed to be so smart, the mind can easily by fooled. For example, it can't seem to tell the difference between real and imagined experience. That's why athletes can dramatically improve their game without ever setting foot on the course or the court. They use mental imagery and visualize perfection over and over.

Maybe nursing can be reprogrammed using affirmations and imagery. A nurse from California gave me this list of affirmations. It's anonymous but someone obviously put a lot of time and thought into it. I wish she or he would step forward and take the credit.

A Nurse's Affirmation

I am a wonderful, capable, competent person.

I believe in myself and my capabilities.

I believe in nursing as an occupational force for social good.

I believe in myself as a valuable member of this occupational force.

I keep myself well-prepared in knowledge and skills and maintain an attitude that allows me to perform to the utmost of my ability.

I believe in nursing as a career, not just a job.

I believe in myself and my nursing colleagues.

I believe that nursing's maximum contribution for social betterment will be achieved through unity maintained within our diversity.

I work to support my colleagues through networking, mentoring, sharing, and valuing others.

I believe in our professional organization as a means of achieving collective power and influence.

I celebrate each achievement made by my nursing colleagues. For every honor for nursing, honors me as well.

Anonymous

Over the years I have become a firm believer in self-fulfilling prophecies. I see it happening all the time. I believe you can program yourself for health and success or for illness and failure. So much is determined by those little gray cells stuffed between your ears.

How do you picture nursing?

How do you picture the typical nurse?

How do you picture yourself in nursing?

Actually, the mind makes a lot of miscalculations. Some of these snafus include catastrophising, all-or-nothing, perfectionism, minimizing, comparative thinking, uncritical acceptance of critics, emotional reasoning, selective editing, personalization, mind reading, and fortune telling.

The following is a description of how each of these mental miscalculations can affect you in general and how they can influence career decisions.

CATASTROPHIZING

Are you an Olympic-class worrier? I used to be. When Gary and I finished graduate school, we moved to Lexington, Kentucky. He did postdoctorate in physics and I taught at a community college.

It was there Gary decided to fulfill his life-long dream and become a pilot. He took flying lessons.

I was terrified of small planes. When he didn't return from his lesson on time, I began to worry. I have a vivid imagination. My thoughts went like this: "Okay, his plane is down. He's dead. I'm a widow. Should I stay in Kentucky? No. It's too far from friends and family. I have a three-year old son to think about. Maybe I'll move back to Rochester, Minnesota. Yes. That's about half-way between both sets of grandparents. Since I went to school there, I'm sure I can get a good job. I'll remarry. This time I'll marry better."

About this time Gary would walk in and I was hysterical. "Why didn't you call? I was worried sick! What if your plane crashed!?!"

Gary just looked at me and said in a matter-of-fact tone, "Would your worrying have kept my plane up?"

"No," I said. I had to smile. It was the last time I worked myself into such a frenzy.

I decided I could either worry or do something constructive. I enrolled in landing lessons. They called them flying lessons but I knew I was only there to learn to land. The fact that I had to learn to take off too was just a minor inconvenience. I took ten hours of instruction. When people would ask me when I was going to solo, I would say, "You don't understand. I will never be up in a plane alone. I am just taking landing lessons."

I knew someday Gary, My Type A husband, would slump over the controls and I would land that plane so smoothly people would marvel. I would walk away without a scratch. And, next time, I would marry better.

Catastrophizing is common in every area of life. I read somewhere that economists had predicted eighteen of the last two recessions. The following example demonstrates what a profound effect catastrophizing can have on important career decisions.

When the hospital decided to computerize, Carole was drafted to help. To her surprise, she seemed to have a natural ability. She caught on quickly and before long was modifying the programs so they were more "nurse friendly."

The software company was so impressed by her ingenuity and teaching ability, they wanted to hire her. She was flustered. This was not a career decision she had ever anticipated.

The salary was attractive. Perhaps too attractive. Carole didn't feel she was worth it. She was overcome with self-doubt. After all, she was a nurse, not a computer specialist. She didn't even have a degree! At that moment she was struggling through a statistics course as part of a BSN completion program and the fact that she was pulling a "C" wasn't doing much for her self-confidence.

The company tried to reassure her that they had all the computer specialists they needed. They wanted her for her nursing expertise. They promised they would train her and team her up with the proper technical people.

But Carole began to catastrophize:

Taking the job would mean moving.

What if I hate living in the East?
What if I don't make any new friends?
What if my family never comes to visit?

Taking the job would mean dropping out of school.

What if there are no BSN completion programs available?
What if the new college program is more expensive?
What if it takes longer?
What if my credits won't transfer?
What if I never finish my degree at all?

Taking the job would mean a total career change.

What if I hate the work?

What if I fail to live up to the company's expectations? What if they fire me!?! And I am stranded, alone in a strange city, with no job, no friends, no family, no money? And I have to come crawling back and admit I am a total failure?

Carole conjured up the worst that could happen, not the best. So, it was a "no-go". She declined the offer.

We've all done what Carole did. Catastrophizing seems to be a normal, even automatic, human response when faced with decisions. Don't you wonder what might have happened if instead of catastrophizing, she had "happilyeverafterized?" Carole does.

What if she had said to herself:

Taking the job would mean moving.

What if I love living in the East?
What if I make great new friends?
What if I meet the man of my dreams?
What if my family visits and we have wonderful times together?

Taking the job would mean dropping out of school.

What if the computer company pays my tuition and gives me release time to finish my degree?
What if the new college is closer, faster, easier and cheaper?
What if they don't require statistics!?!
What if I even go on to graduate school?

Taking the job would mean a total career change.

What if I love my new job?
What if I become a computer genius?
What if I invent stuff that will help nurses improve patient care?
What if I exceed the company's expectations and am rapidly promoted?
What if I make tons of money and have to wear designer clothes, take European vacations, and drive an exotic car?

Happilyeverafterizing is not a normal response when faced with a decision. Unlike catastrophizing it does not occur spontaneously but must be systematically undertaken so the good possibilities can be coaxed out and examined.

If you are having trouble, list the worst things that could possibly happen. For each item on the worst list, construct a positive counterpart, the best things that could possibly happen.

WORST	BEST
____________________	____________________
____________________	____________________
____________________	____________________
____________________	____________________
____________________	____________________

Any career decision is a guess. At best, it is an educated guess. When you catch yourself catastrophizing, stop. Start over. Begin fantasizing about the best that could possibly happen. Then ask yourself how you can "eliminate the negative and latch on the affirmative."

ALL-OR-NOTHING

Primary nursing is a good example. It was meant to be a philosophy, not an ultimatum. Yet nurses seem to feel if they haven't done absolutely everything for a patient from oral care to brain transplants, they've done next to nothing.

We whine about overwork but are reluctant to delegate. We can't even let go of non-nursing tasks. They have to be pried out of our fingers.

Once I addressed the Emergency Nurses Association convention in San Francisco. Not only had they convened the session at 7:30 a.m. on a Saturday, they had sponsored a fitness run at 5:30 a.m.! I walked into the ballroom thinking no group other than nurses would schedule conventions in such a brutal fashion. I also wondered how many would show up. To my delight, I found a couple thousand wildly enthusiastic emergency nurses raring to go.

The subject was Walk-On-Water Women. (Doing it all, having it all, being it all and working miracles in our spare time.) It seemed especially appropriate because one ENA chapter was selling mugs emblazoned with "I Save Lives for a Living."

We had a romping, stomping good time. When I finished, some of the participants gathered at the front to chat. One nurse dashed back to her room and brought me the sweatshirt she had worn on the morning run. Apologizing for its being slightly used, she presented it to me as a gift saying, "After listening to you I knew you just had to have this shirt!"

On the sweatshirt was a cat sliding down a wall leaving claw marks all the way. Next to the cat it said, **"Everything I Ever Let Go of Had Claw Marks All Over It!"** I treasure that shirt.

Nurses go full throttle and then are surprised when they collapse or their careers crash and burn.

"I work for a doctor between 45-50 hours a week. When he asked me to work even more hours, I felt too guilty to refuse. I also felt guilty leaving my family to fend for themselves. So I would stay up until 1:00 a.m. trying to maintain a perfect house, baking cookies, preparing meals, doing the laundry, etc. I wanted them to have what they were used to. Then I'd put in a 10-11 hour workday.

I lasted about three months. I felt like I was getting an ulcer. I felt like crying all the time for no apparent reason. I had tachycardia. I would get anxious and easily upset over minor things at home (never at work).

Deciding I could no longer go on this way, I resigned. Now I am in a less stressful situation and work only 30 hours a week. It is the best choice I could have made. Life is too short and kids grow up too fast. I am enjoying each day now and not just trying to survive until Friday."

A nurse who attempted a career transition into the business world wrote:

"When I was offered the job of retail store manager, I was flattered and excited. I had a lot of support from my husband, children, and friends. Then the job became more and more demanding. Soon I was putting in 80 hours a week. The stress of no longer being able to meet all the needs of my family was intense. I was overwhelmed with much guilt and frustration.

Hurt, confused, and resentful, I finally quit. For a long time I felt I never wanted to work at ANY paying job outside the home. I felt I had failed.

Now I'm back working part-time as a nurse. I still wonder if I made the right decision. That may have been the start of a good career. Now I feel I just have a job."

What on earth makes a nurse think she can work 80 hours a week and not burn out?

Nurses think in extremes: All or Nothing. Win or Lose. Now or Never. Family or Career. Just because you can't complete your education now doesn't mean you never will. Just because you can't work full-time doesn't mean you can't make a significant contribution part-time.

PERFECTIONISM

Perfectionism is a close cousin of all-or-nothing. It leads to procrastination which leads to paralysis. A nurse hesitates to apply for an opening because she fears she is not "perfect" for the job. Job advertisements usually list *ideal* qualifications even though the agency placing the ad knows that finding an exact fit will be next to impossible. If you have two out of three, or three out of five of the most desired qualifications, apply. It's good experience. And who knows? You just might get the job.

When you step into a new role, don't expect to be perfect. Remember there is a big difference between temporary and permanent incompetence. Be patient with yourself.

One morning while beachcombing in northern Oregon, I was saddened to see thousands of dead crabs washed ashore. I thought something catastrophic had happened. It made me wax philosophically about the meaning of life.

A college biology teacher friend quickly set me straight. They were not dead crabs. They were crab shells. Crabs have to shed their shells in order to grow. (How would I know? I grew up in Iowa.)

She also told me there is a period of time before the new shell hardens when the crab is extremely vulnerable. When you've shed your old shell, expect to feel vulnerable. And don't be surprised if you feel a bit "crabby."

OVERGENERALIZATION

Overgeneralization is taking a single event and extrapolating it to all events. Let's say you've finally written that article for professional publication. Just because one journal rejects it does not mean all journals will reject it. There are wonderful stories about books that were rejected by dozens of publishers before going on to becoming best sellers. Be persistent. Don't let one rejection slip stop you.

Gwen applied for a Vice President of Nursing position. Weeks went by and she had not been called for an interview. This seemed strange because she had been encouraged to apply by the chairman of the board. When they bumped into each other at a social function, she asked how the job search was going. He was surprised her application had not evoked action. Shortly afterward she was called for an interview.

The moment she sat down with the CEO, she knew this interview had not been his idea. She was being stonewalled and she didn't know why. His cryptic comments soon gave her a clue. It was her Ph.D. that was bugging him. Her predecessor had also been doctorally prepared. On paper she was perfect but she could not produce in the real world. He had been burned once and was not about to be burned again.

She motioned for a time out and suggested they get down to brass tacks. While listing examples of concrete accomplishments as vice president of another hospital, she handed him her business card. "This might interest you," she said. A broad smile came over his face. Her business card did not say "Ph.D." That completely won him over.

The interview was salvaged. She got the job. And she produced! In the first six months, she saved the hospital several million dollars. Today they are a fantastic team. Yet none of this would have happened if she hadn't challenged the CEO's overgeneralization of doctorally prepared candidates.

MINIMIZING

There's a wonderful line in a country-western song that goes, "I've been rearranging chairs on a ship that's going down." Minimizing is like doing interior decorating on the Titanic.

A woman, about to marry a man on death row, gushes to a TV talk show host, "I know he's a mass murderer, but he has such beautiful eyes." Eyes??? The man's a murderer!

A good friend of mine became a paralegal after her daughters finished college. She went to work for a couple of young lawyers whom she liked enormously and thought had great potential. Even though signs of gross financial mismanagement were obvious from the very beginning, she chose to overlook them.

For two years she helped trim costs, juggled accounts, smoothed things over with irate creditors, and struggled to meet payroll. When they asked her to out-and-out lie for them she finally came to her senses and quit. They still owe her four month's salary. They may have been personable with lots of potential but they were pond scum.

Know when to jump ship. Eileen went to work for a private psychiatric hospital shortly after graduation. The building and grounds were beautiful but the company skimped on staffing.

By the end of her first year the hospital was in serious financial difficulty. They cut back even further on staff and exhorted everyone to go the extra mile and get they through the "temporary" monetary crisis. Eileen was working 60 hours a week. She was exhausted and frantic that patients were not receiving proper care. Then the hospital announced salary cuts. Still Eileen did not quit. It was like being caught in a whirlpool. There was no way to go but down. Several agonizing months later the hospital folded. So did Eileen. She did not work as a nurse for the next five years.

Minimizing also has another meaning and that is not giving yourself credit for your talents, abilities, and accomplishments. Attributing your success to luck, fate, or the whim of the gods, can undermine your confidence. Frank Lloyd Wright, the famous architect, said early in his career he had to decide between hypocritical humility and honest arrogance. He chose honest arrogance.

COMPARATIVE THINKING

It's normal to look at others to figure out how you're doing. Fortunately, someone is always doing worse than you are. Unfortunately, someone is always doing better. It doesn't matter whether you are comparing cars, curls, clothes, children, or cash. However, if your hobby is comparing yourself with people to whom you can never measure up, you're going to be perpetually depressed.

Resist the urge to take someone else's success and use it as evidence of your failure. For example, when attending nurse-of-the-year banquets, do you ever find yourself sinking lower and lower into your chair? As the virtues and accomplishments of the award-winning nurse are read from the podium, do you ever think, "Ooooo, I'm such a loooooser! What have I been doing with all my time?"

There are stellar nurses and there are so-so nurses. Most of us fall somewhere in between. Go for your personal best. Don't put yourself in competition with your colleqgues. Enjoy the banquets and the ceremonies. Be happy for the winners and take pride that we are all part of the nursing profession. Life is not a contest. Neither is nursing.

UNCRITICAL ACCEPTANCE OF CRITICS

Does it irk you when a movie, book, or restaurant you like receives an unfavorable review? It irks me. I'm still trying to figure out how a person becomes a professional critic.

A condescending article on Norman Rockwell claimed he was not an artist, he was an illustrator (shudder!). It sounded like professional jealousy to me. There are days when I think Siskel and Ebert should be required to produce a perfect movie before we allow them to review anything else. And, if the JCAHO is so smart, let them buy a hospital their own and run it. Wouldn't it be nice to survey them for a change?

When you are criticized consider the source. Is the person qualified to judge you or your actions? Even if they are, you have the right to constructive criticism. Don't roll over and play dead. If you feel their criticism is unfair, confront them. Kate and Audrey were both head nurses. Kate continuously criticized Audrey's performance. She nitpicked, belittled, and challenged every action or decision. "If this were *my* unit..." was her favorite phrase.

Sick of constant harrassment, Audrey handed Kate her keys one day saying, "Obviously you think you can do a much better job of running my unit than I can. It's all yours! I could use some time off." She turned and walked away.

Kate ran after her apologizing and begging her to take her keys and her unit back. That was the end of the criticism.

An irate physician phoned demanding to speak to "the **twit** in charge of the floor." The flustered nurse who answered the phone replied, "She's not here."

When the head nurse returned from lunch, she was told how angry the doctor was and how he wanted to speak to the twit in charge. She called back telling the doctor's receptionist that "This is the **twit** from Four West. I'm returning the doctor's call."

It was the receptionist's turn to be flustered. Since the head nurse refused to give her name, she had to tell the doctor it was the twit.

It was the doctor's turn to be flustered. He had to laugh. He apologized. They cleared up the misunderstanding and, ever since that incident, have been great friends.

SELECTIVE EDITING

A syndicated columnist receives a monthly report listing the number of newspapers carrying his work, the number cancelling his column, and the number picking it up for the first time.When one newspaper cancels, he says he is thrown for a loop. He frets. He worries. "Am I losing my edge?"

The fact that over 600 newspapers are still carrying his column and a dozen more have just been brought on line, doesn't seem to reassure him.

I found his comments comforting. Early in my career as a professional speaker, I would pour over the evaluations. I would toss aside those that gave me good or excellent ratings and zero in on the critical ones. I fretted. I worried. Evaluations depressed me.

Eventually, I came to accept the fact that I could please all the people some of the time and some of the people all the time. I could not please all the people all the time. Today I know that 90 of 100 people attending my workshop will think I was good or great, nine will think I was okay, and one will think I'm bug spit. I console myuself by thinking the person who circled 1's instead of 5's is dyslexic.

We often discount our abilities and lock on to our limitations. When you drive home after a hard day at the hospital, are you congratulating yourself for all the tasks you accomplished or mentally listing the tasks that were left undone? Are you delighted about all the patients and families you helped or depressed about the one patient or family you couldn't help that day?

PERSONALIZATION

You get caught in a traffic jam or in the slow line at the grocery store and you kick yourself. Why me? Why is it always me? It has nothing to do with you. Don't take it personally.

A woman sitting in the back row at one of my seminars looked awfully unhappy. Throughout the day I played to that woman, trying to get her involved, trying to lighten her mood. No success. I figured she would give me a lousy evaluation but suddenly there she was shaking my hand and saying, "This is the best seminar I have ever attended. You said in six hours what it took me three years in therapy to learn. Thank you!"

She was still in therapy. She was still depressed. It had nothing to do with me or with the seminar; yet all day long I had taken her unhappiness personally.

Here's a situation described by a young manager:

When Katherine returned to our organization after an extended absence, she was offered her old management position but turned it down. I was offered the position and accepted.

On this particular occasion I made a scheduling decision and then went to lunch. When I returned she had changed everything involved in my decision and ordered other things done. I was new in this job and had less work experience in this area than she did. I was so angry I couldn't react rationally. I did nothing. When the day was over, I went home frustrated, angry, crying, and wanting to do grave bodily harm to someone.

Whenever I use this example in workshops, participants invariably jump to the same conclusion the young manager did: Katherine is out to get me.

Instead of taking it personally, find out what was going on in Katherine's mind. Approach it in a non-threatening way. "I see the schedule has been changed." Then zip your lip. Perhaps Katherine has just done you a huge favor.

If she is trying to undermine your power, take her aside for a long talk. Actually, the long talk should have occurred before the two of you began working together. You should have gone out to lunch and discussed potential problems.

While some managers do have trouble surrendering the reins to the new manager, others are thrilled to get out of the driver's seat. They are tired of the hassles of being in charge.

Because I often deal with disillusioned, disgruntled nurses, I am pleasantly surprised when I meet a nurse bubbling over with enthusiasm for the profession. Especially when that nurse has been "on duty" 20 years or more. Joyce was such a nurse.

She hadn't always felt this enthusiastic about nursing. In fact, for about seven years she was utterly miserable. For seven years she was a head nurse.

Joyce worked as a staff nurse in labor and delivery for a dozen years. When the head nurse position opened up, she was encouraged to accept it. She had seniority, everyone respected her skills, and she was popular. She was flattered and accepted the job.

Unfortunately, Joyce was a square peg in a round hole. She was trying to force herself into a slot for which she simply did not have the aptitude. At first she chalked it up to inexperience.

She thought things would improve with time. They did but she didn't. She became increasingly unhappy.

She began to dread work. Her days were filled with meetings, paperwork, budgets, schedules, and grievances. There was almost no patient contact. Struggling to keep her staff happy, she felt she must be available around the clock. Her answering machine became a monster, constantly bringing her bad news, but she couldn't bring herself to pull the plug. Work took precedence over everything else. She had almost no personal life.

Finally, she reached the point where she was crying before she went to work in the morning and crying after she finished work in the evening. She felt physically ill and began to have serious doubts about her sanity.

Something drastic had to be done. She decided to quit nursing. She just couldn't take it anymore. Then reality intruded. What else could she do for a living? She had been a nurse forever. She had been with the same hospital almost 20 years. If she left, she would lose most of her pension and all of her benefits.

She asked herself when she had last been happy in nursing. It was when she was a staff nurse. She had loved nursing then. Maybe she could learn to love it again. The next day she resigned her management post and took a staff position in postpartum. The crying jags stopped. Her physical symptoms disappeared.

That was a year ago. Today she looks forward to going to work every day. She has a rich, full, active life off duty as well. Best of all, she gave her answering machine to her daughter. Joyce says some people still don't recognize her because when she was a head nurse she never smiled. Now she smiles all the time.

MIND READING

Nurses sometimes seem to have a sixth sense. We anticipate people's needs. We're quick. We move in and meet needs people don't even know they have. Then we despair when they are not properly grateful.

Our heightened sensitivity leads us to believe we can actually read minds. We are distraught when we fail to do so. When a friend or family member or patient commits suicide, we can't believe we missed the signs and signals. We beat ourselves up emotionally, fearful we are not the competent professionals we pretend to be.

We also expect other people to be equally sensitive and read our minds. We expect our spouse or our supervisor to anticipate our needs and meet them before being asked.

Loren was surprised when Ann mentioned her interest in a position that had just been filled. When asked why she hadn't applied, Ann said, "They knew where I was. If they had wanted me, they would have asked."

There are no true mind readers.

Whatever you want personally or professionally, you are going to have to speak up and ask for it.

FORTUNE TELLING

We think we should be able to predict the future. "I should have seen it coming!" We kick ourselves because we should have bought stock in Xerox when it was a dollar a share, chosen another profession, or married a different person.

Sometimes I arrive at the airport in time to catch an earlier flight. As I stand there, the following scenario flashes through my mind with the speed of light.

Okay, I trade in my tickets for the earlier flight. The plane goes into a crash-and-burn spiral. All the way into the ground I am saying, "Why? Why did I change my tickets? If God wanted me on this flight I would have been scheduled for this flight. I could have been perfectly safe but **no** I had to change my tickets!" Splat!

Okay. I stand pat. I keep my original tickets and board my scheduled flight. The plane goes into a crash-and-burn spiral. All the way into the ground I am saying, "Why? Why didn't I change my tickets? God got me to the airport early. He said, 'Look up, Melodie, you can get on another flight!' Did I listen? No!" Splat!

Because I cannot predict the future, I make the best decision on the information I have. I take the earlier flight because it will get me to my destination sooner.

You may be kicking yourself because you did not go to the right school or did not continue your education years ago. You should have known you would want to be in management or education or research. You should have known you would need your bachelor's or master's or doctorate.

When you chose your profession, your job, your spouse, you made the the best decision you could on the information you had. Stop flogging yourself emotionally for your "mistake." None of us can predict the future.

It doesn't help to question how you got here. **You are here.** The only question that matters is, "What next?"

What Next?

1. Are you a ground hugger or a high flyer? What do you think your life equation should add up to?

2. List a dozen adjectives to describe each of the following:

A. Nursing:

B. The typical nurse:

C. Yourself as a nurse:

3. Are the adjectives you used positive or negative? Try this exercise with your colleagues.

4. Give a personal and a professional example for each of the common mental miscalculations:

Catastrophizing
All-or-Nothing
Perfectionism
Minimizing
Uncritical Acceptance of Critics
Emotional Reasoning
Selective Editing
Personalization
Mind Reading
Fortune Telling

5. Take a thin gold elastic cord, the kind that comes on gift boxes, and tie a bow around your wrist. The next time you catch yourself making one of those mental miscalculations, snap that cord on the inside of your wrist. Ouch! It smarts! And it makes you smarter. You begin to realize how frequently this happens. Then you can interrupt the negative cycle and take corrective measures.

TOO POOPED TO PUCKER

Halfway through a workshop focusing on strategies for professional success, a tall, lanky woman with a depressed-frazzled look approached me. The group had just gone through a goal-setting exercise in which each nurse had written a goal to be accomplished in 6-12 months, along with her name and phone number. They had then exchanged goals with a nurse they did not know.

"I didn't write down my real goal," she said. "I was afraid."

"Oh? Would you like to share your real goal with me?" (I was hoping she wouldn't reveal anything too personal or too painful. It is difficult to deal with anything complicated during a fifteen minute break.)

Words began to tumble out. "I want to quit my job. I want to move to Vermont. That's what I really want. But I couldn't write that—my boss is sitting right beside me! She wouldn't understand. No one understands. I don't know what to do." She rambled on about all the pros and cons. Her confusion and indecision had obviously overwhelmed her.

I knew the next segment of the workshop dealt with making tough decisions so I asked her to hang in awhile longer. Help was on the way. I encouraged her to come talk to me when the workshop was over.

The next couple of hours I crammed in everything I could think of to expedite decisions. As I watched her face visibly brighten, I was feeling rather smug. I knew this information would help her.

After the workshop she enthusiastically shook my hand. I asked which part of the decision-making theory had helped her most.

"No, it wasn't that," she said to my surprise. "It was something else you said. It was when you quoted Coach Vince Lombardi saying, 'Fatigue makes cowards of us all.' I knew right away that was it. **Fatigue!** I've been so tired for so long. I can't even remember not feeling tired. No wonder I can't make decisions. No wonder I feel depressed. I'm going to get 'untired'—no more overtime, no more working on my days off, no more committee assignments. I'm going to let my grown kids fend for themselves. I'm going to fend for me for a change." She left, grinning from ear to ear.

Another nurse writing about the conflict she was experiencing trying to balance family and career wrote, "I often wonder when the day will come that I don't wake up in the morning feeling totally exhausted."

Fatigue interferes with careers. Fatigue can keep a nurse from making or carrying out career plans. It is a factor we have not taken accurately into account when discussing nurses and nursing.

How often have you heard disparaging remarks about how little career commitment nurses have? Comments like: we treat nursing as a "job" and not a "profession," we put in our time but nothing more, we lack involvement, ambition, vision, commitment.

Before making or believing comments like that, take a look at the big picture. Nurses are 97 percent female and statistically 90 percent of us will conceive and bear children. We're wives. We're mothers. We're nurses. And we're tired—often down to the bone tired. It is not that we *lack* commitment. We are overcommitted.

Women in our society continue to do double duty. In her excellent book, **The Second Shift**, Arlie Hochschild says women are putting in a full month of 24-hour days more each year than men do. That is calculated on a 15-hour per week leisure gap between men and women.

When I use the phrase "second shift," every working woman knows exactly what I'm talking about. The typical male returns home after a hard day at work, sits down, puts his feet up, reads the paper, watches the evening news, and calls over his shoulder, "Hey, Hon, what's for dinner?"

The typical female returns home after a hard day at work, puts on her Reeboks and shoves into high gear. She's stirring the stew, doing laundry, checking homework, making a costume for the school play, wondering if she mailed the check for the mortgage, mopping up a spill with her left foot, and the dog is in heat!

Working women seem to get up earlier and stay up later than any other family member.

Think about what you do on your days off. Most of us just work twice as hard. We scramble and scurry trying to catch up on projects, errands, and housework. Having days off mid-week is both a blessing and a curse. It often means the nurse has a lengthy list of nuisance tasks assigned to her by every other member of the family.

On her day off, Mary Lynn picked up her long *"To Do"* list and sighed. She just couldn't muster up any enthusiasm. She tossed the list back on the table and proceeded to enjoy her day off. She went to the art museum, met a friend for lunch, and caught an early movie.

When her husband came home he began to ask questions: Did you get the oil changed? Did you call about the insurance company's overcharge? Did you pick up my suit at the cleaners? She kept answering "No."

Finally he said in an icy tone, "Good Lord, what did you do all day? You were supposed to take care of these things. After all, it was your day off!"

She snapped back, "Yes, it was my day **off** and I took it **OFF**!" A major 'discussion' followed. They both realized that she never really had a day off. On his days off, he played golf or went fishing. She just kept working. Their solution was to have her cut back to four days a week at work. She took the fifth day and did whatever she wanted to do. No questions asked.

There are other problems that plague nurses. Many of us are required to rotate shifts. That not only means sleep disturbances but also poor eating habits, both of which contribute to fatigue. Our workloads are unpredictable. Crisis is commonplace. We are often pushed beyond our physical and emotional limits by high acuity and low staffing.

Nurses take care of people on duty. Nurses take care of people off duty. Nurses take care of everyone but themselves.

Here's an excellent example:

"I work in a setting where the paper turnover at the end of the month is tremendous. Care plans, prescriptions, medication sheets, individualized treatment programs—all must be updated and computerized by midnight at the end of the month (every month).

I worked on the last day of the month my 10-hour shift and was unable to complete my assignment as I had other emergencies and staffing problems to deal with that day.

I went home. Fixed supper. Bathed my 2 and 4-year olds and put them to bed.

Meanwhile my husband went to play tennis with a friend. And I encouraged it thinking it would be good for him to get out and relax.

In my mind I planned to go back to work when he got home.

He stopped in around 8:30 p.m. and asked if he could go have a beer with his friend. I again told him it was OK and I proceeded to do some laundry to pass the time.

At midnight he came home. I was upset and crying. Feeling angry with myself for not being assertive. We had an argument and then I left and went to work to finish my paper tasks that needed to be completed.

I felt overburdened.

I felt angry with myself.

I felt tired and stressed.

I felt that I gave 100 percent to my marriage and my husband gave much less.

I worked through feelings in my mind that I am the breadwinner, cook, cleaner, wife, mother, etc.

I went home and apologized for not being assertive. He also apologized and I felt better."

Just for a moment try picturing this scenario in reverse. Your husband puts in a hectic 10-hour shift, comes home, fixes dinner, bathes and feeds the toddlers, and puts them to bed. Meanwhile you have been playing tennis with a friend, which he encouraged thinking it would be good for you to get out and relax. At 8:30 p.m. you stop in and ask if you can go have a beer with your friend. He proceeds to tidy up and do some laundry to pass the time.

If you're not giggling by now, you've lost your sense of humor. The whole scene is ludicrous. It would never happen. But wouldn't it be wonderful if it did? Wouldn't it be wonderful if women were encouraged to play as hard as they work?

Career planning requires time and energy. For many nurses those commodities are almost non-existent. What about you? Are you too pooped to pucker...or to plan?

What Next?

1. Circle where are you on this Fatigue Scalewith 1 being a catatonic stupor and a 10 being a whirling dirvish

<■■■■■■■■■■■■■■■■■■■■■■■■■■■■■>

1 2 3 4 5 6 7 8 9 10

2. How many hours of leisure do you have per week:

3. Describe how you usually spend your day off:

4. What do you do to get *untired*? What do you do for fun? What do you do to recharge your batteries? Fill in What-I-Do-For-Fun form on the next page. Be specific.

What I Do For Fun

WHITHER THOU GOEST, I WILL GO

While career planning is not easy for anyone, it is probably more complicated for women than for men. Unless a woman is a friendless, unmarried, sterile orphan, she will scrutinize any career decision in light of its impact on personal relationships.

Women are expected to put family first and career second. Men are expected to do the opposite. They are allowed to make unilateral career decisions, taking for granted that their wives and families will adapt. Here's an astonishing example of one-sided career planning. The names of the states have been changed to protect the innocent.

"After living here 16 months, my husband came to me at the hospital and said, "I just took a new job. We are moving to Nebraska. Can you get off work tonight to go look for a place to live?"

I was stunned We were to start building a house that next week! I had a job I loved, good friends, was active in my church, etc. In an instant, I was to put all this aside to shift my whole life to Nebraska.

Barely settled, one year later, my husband said, "We are moving back to Arizona. How soon can you be ready to move (i.e. sell the house, find a new house, get a new job, etc.)? I have to be there in one week!"

"UGH! This situation is still not resolved as we are just beginning to settle in here again."

There is a double standard when it comes to career planning. If you doubt it, just try reading the above scenario with the roles reversed. It is unimaginable.

Women, unpredictably uprooted, hesitate to make career plans. Why bother? It just leads to disappointment.

As dual-career couples become the rule, not the exception, it becomes extremely important to do career planning together. Any move must be mutually beneficial. If not, it may mean not only the end of a career; it may mean the end of a marriage.

"I had been married for several years, had moved multiple times to different parts of the country and changed employers so that my husband could be successful in his career.

I was finally at a place were I was happy, moving positively in my career with many friends. My husband, however, after many bad experiences in jobs, became unemployed again. He decided he wanted to move and obtained another job across the country. He couldn't understand when I refused to budge from my home, friends, and career once again. I was 'inflexible'!!! I had had enough and finally took a stand. I think he was afraid and threatened by my successful career, and thought another move would 'stop me,' giving him a chance to get ahead as he felt he should be.

Unfortunately, our discussions and counseling led to dissolving the marriage—but I'm happier than ever!"

Just as this woman practiced "whither thou goest" for years, many a woman has neglected or sabotaged her own career trying to promote or protect her husband's. Our culture dictates that the man be the head of the family and the primary breadwinner. It may be a ridiculous rule, but it is a rule. And when a rule is broken, someone is made to feel guilty.

Financially successful women are often overtly and covertly punished. In the following example, a husband **says** he is pleased with his wife's success, but his actions reveal his true feelings.

"My husband says he's glad I make more money than he does for a change but whenever I stay late at work or get called in, he pouts and gets very angry. He feels that I don't really "work" at

work. He thinks I get to sit around and talk with my co-workers and that's why I'm late and/or spend 2-3 hours when I get called into the hospital."

Traditions die hard. Even when a woman's salary equals or exceeds her husband's, she is expected to behave as if she is the secondary earner. Here is a nurse who is much more successful financially than her husband. Notice how he undermines her success by pointing out her inability to cope with all the household chores and, horror of horrors, neglecting her wifely duties.

"I am the major wage earner in the family as my husband has little post high school education. In fact, his wages are much less than mine. Yet with my working full time, caring for two children (ages 2 years and 4 months), and doing all the housework, he acts like he's doing me a favor when he helps out. When I ask him to do something specific (i.e. move the laundry from the washer to the dryer), he reminds me it's my job. His major complaint now is that I'm always too tired for him. He says he knows I have to work to support us but sometimes I wonder if he really believes what he's saying."

Relationships are of paramount importance to women. If a career choice remotely threatens a relationship, a woman will usually decline. Her career must never even **inconvenience** husband or children.

"After a day at work and a night class at the university, I came home to find my husband and son in front of the TV complaining, 'What's for supper—there's nothing to eat around here.'

I explained I had left soup in the refrigerator and there was all sorts of material for salads (untossed so of course inedible). We live three blocks from a large supermarket so I suggested if they didn't like soup, they could have gone shopping.

I had had a great day, had a perfect paper returned to me in class that night and when I heard 'there's nothing to eat'—I blew up! My husband and I had a ***major discussion*** *and after three weeks we are still* ***discussing*** *our roles.*

That night I did not fix supper. My husband has not grocery shopped in the ten years we've been married and he never will. But we've reached some common ground. I refuse to shop more than once a week and I will buy frozen meals which he can prepare on the nights I have class. If there's nothing available, he will need to eat out or make other arrangements."

What have we done to the men in our lives that they can no longer forage for food?!? If her husband has not been in the grocery store for ten years, he is in for severe sticker shock.

One man kept exhorting his wife to get food costs under control. He couldn't understand why she couldn't be more thrifty. Then he changed to a teaching position which gave him the summer off. He decided to manage the household. He would show his wife how to be more efficient.

His stated goal was to feed a family of four on $50 a week. After his first visit to the grocery store, he scrapped that idea. By the end of the summer, he had come to admire how well his wife had managed everything over the years.

When discussing this example in workshops, I used to suggest if Macho Man wouldn't grocery shop, he should go out and shoot something to eat. After this next example came in, however, I decided to withdraw that advice.

"It is hunting season. My husband informed me not to expect anything of him or plan anything for him for four months (October-January). This is deer season. We have two children (5 and 2). I work full-time as a nurse. He works 3-11. He says I will have to find another sitter on the weekends I work because that's the only time he can hunt in the evenings.

He can't even take the trash out before leaving at 4 a.m. as the neighbor's dog gets in it. He still expects me to do all the cleaning, pack his lunch, care for kids, do laundry, cooking, shopping, errands, etc. The holiday season is always a disaster. He doesn't understand why I'm so stressed."

Imagine a woman going to her husband and saying, "Don't expect anything of me or plan anything for me for the next four months. That's when the White Sales will be. Find a sitter if you have to work on the weekends because that's the only time I can shop in the evenings."

The religious overtones of "whither thou goest" make career planning for some women seem almost blasphemous.

"I am under attack by well-meaning women from my church because I have a career. They tell me it is my God-given duty to stay home and accept my role as a mother. They keep bringing me books which say things like 'the family is the longest lasting group of people that ever existed and is now nearly disintegrated because of the mothers refusing to accept and take responsibility in the home.' I don't know how to resolve this dilemma."

Ah, guilt! In the Victorian era, women were expected to tolerate sex but they were certainly not to enjoy it. Today's women are expected to tolerate jobs, but they are certainly not to enjoy them.

Mindsets like "a woman's place is in the home," also make career planning difficult.

"I had three small pre-school children. I didn't have a paying job. My husband didn't want me to have a job. He thought the woman's place was in the home. I became depressed. Thought of suicide.

Finally I told him I needed to get out of the house. I needed to work.

He decided I should go to school. He didn't want his wife working in a 'hamburger joint' or something similar. He did let me choose what type of schooling I would get. I believe he thought by the time I graduated I would have it out of my system.

I went to nursing school. God handled the outcome. My husband died while I was in school. I have never regretted taking my stand to work."

It is not just the economy that makes career planning for women essential. It is the fact that the vast majority of us will be widowed and/or divorced during our lifetimes. All of us need to be able to make it on our own.

No matter how wonderful your husband is, he cannot promise you undying love. Women continue to outlive men by almost eight years. So if you and your husband are the same age, statistically speaking, you can plan on about eight years of widowhood. If you were foolish enough to marry a man older than you, take the difference between your ages and add eight years to get some idea of how long you may have to fend for yourself.

To pursue a career often means investing in higher education. Many women have sacrificed to help their husbands through college. They've moved, worked two jobs, scrimped and saved, delayed having children, and gone without creature comforts. Their husband's goal was their goal.

What happens when it is the wife that wants to continue her education?

"I want to get my master's degree. To do this I MUST move. My husband says, 'Go away wherever you want to achieve your goal.' He will stay here with the children (ages 13, 8, 6).

I feel I am selfish to want this and would be deserting my family. He won't move or leave his job for me. But if the roles were reversed, undoubtedly, I would."

Would your husband move or leave his job to enable you to pursue your career? It is an interesting question. How much support can you count on?

Here's a wonderful example of a husband's support for his wife's career:

A nursing instructor with two young school-aged children began working on her master's degree. She was soon overwhelmed with the demands of work, school, and family. Like so many other women, she did not discontinue any of her former activities; she just added graduate school on top.

Her husband, a physician, became alarmed at the toll the stress was taking. He sat her down for a heart-to-heart talk. Knowing how important her education was to her continued teaching in nursing, he suggested they make some changes.

The housekeeper came every week instead of every two weeks. They found a high school girl to run errands and help with laundry and other chores. Her husband dropped out of a volleyball league, resigned from a couple of committees, and stopped moonlighting in the emergency room so he would be more available for the children.

When she told him how guilty all this was making her feel, he said, "My education was for 'us' and your education is for 'us.' We're in this together."

What Next?

1. Read this chapter with the one you love and discuss the situations.
2. Jot down a sentence or two about how "whither thou goest" has influenced the direction of your career:

   ____
   ____
   ____
   ____

3. Take a sheet of paper and describe three things you would like to accomplish in your career over the next 2 to 5 years. Have your spouse (or most important other person in your life) do the same. Lay the two sheets side by side.
   a. Are there any surprises?
   b. Which ones are compatible and which will put the two of you in conflict?
   c. List three concrete ways you can help each other:

   I can help you by...

   (1) ____________________________

   (2) ____________________________

   (3) ____________________________

You can help me by...

(1) ______________________________

(2) ______________________________

(3) ______________________________

d. Discuss how either of your plans might be sabotaged:

Internally:

Externally:

4. Calculate how many years of widowhood you can expect by taking the difference between your ages and adding 8 years.

5. Next time marry a younger man!

RESEARCH
RESEARCH PROJECT

HAPPILY EVER AFTER

work (wurk) n.

While any dictionary will give dozens of definitions and different usages for the word **work**, to many people it is just another four-letter word. Almost an expletive.

Perhaps that's because it is usually contrasted with play. Work is the negative end of the continuum while play is the positive. The synonyms given for work do not improve its image: labor, toil, drudgery, and travail. Such synonyms imply work is strenuous, fatuguing, dull, wearisome, monotonous, sometimes demeaning, and involves great effort, pain, or suffering. Work sounds like something to avoid like the plague.

A Roper Organization Poll revealed a rather dramatic change in the work ethic. People used to say the purpose of leisure was to recharge their batteries so they could do a better job at work. Now they say the purpose of work is to give them more and better leisure time.

One nurse described her hectic lifestyle, complaining that work ate up the majority of each day and concluded by saying, "All I have to live for is the weekend. I feel like I throw away five days a week to get two."

Do you feel your life is being "thrown away," that work is interfering with rather than enhancing your life? Does work for you mean labor, toil, and drudgery? Is your job strenuous, fatiguing, dull, wearisome, and monotonous?

If it is, then you'd better do something fast because work is here to stay. Let's be realistic. You have about as much chance of going through life without working as you have going through life without eating. Instead of trying to get out of work, try to get into work that better suits you.

Easier said than done? Not necessarily.

If the following sounds like a commercial for anther book, it is. I highly recommend you get your hands on copy of Kathy Kolbe's **The Conative Connection** (Addition Wesley, 1991) if you want to work happily ever after.

I bought it primarily because of its subtitle, "Uncovering the Link Between Who You Are and How You Perform," thinking it might be useful for nurse managers. The first time I tried to read it, however, I just couldn't seem to concentrate. The vocabulary and the concepts are a bit unusual and I have the attention span of a gnat. So I shelved it.

Three months went by and I was about to leave for Denver to do a workshop for nurse managers. As I searched my bookcase for something to take along, **The Conative Connection** beckoned to me. I thought, "Well, if it's the only book I take and I strap myself in at the 37,000 feet, maybe I can polish it off."

I strapped myself in and began to read. To keep my mind from wandering, I began to outline and make notes. By the time I reached Denver I had worked through most of the book and I was so excited I could hardly contain myself. It was truly an "AHA!" experience.

When I addressed the managers the next morning, I just had to share what I'd learned. I spent about 15 minutes describing conation and watched their reaction. It struck a responsive chord. You could almost see light bulbs going on all over the room. I tried the introductory teaser in a half dozen workshop groups with nurses from different specialties. The reaction was the same. Fascination. Relief. Excitement.

Thanks to **The Conative Connection** I suddenly understood all the mysteries of the universe. I knew why nursing education and nursing practice would never be more compatible than they are today, why time management experts would never go hungry, and why graduate school could make you sick. I even knew why I didn't have a garage.

Curious? Good!

Don't be surprised it the word "conative" (pronounced with a long "o") doesn't ring a bell. You can find it in the *Dictionary of the 1000 Most Obscure Words in the English Language*.

Evidently we have known from ancient times that there are three parts of the human mind: the cognitive, which means to know, the affective, which means to feel, and the conative, which means to act. Scholars and researchers have concentrated on the first two. Yet without conation there is no action.

Kolbe says conation has nothing to do with what we think, feel, wish, hope, know, or value. It is not correlated with age, training, education, experience, intellect, personality, or genetics.

What does it have to do with? A knack. Your knack for getting things done. According to Kolbe conation has to do with how you most naturally deal with detail, structure, risk, and problem solving along with how you use time and energy.

Conation is not about what you **can** or **can't do**. Much more importantly, it is about what you **will** or **won't do**. And it is bedrock. It is something that does not change. It remains a constant over the lifespan.

When I read it was "bedrock," my initial reaction was, "That's depressing!" As a mental health professional, I want to believe everyone can change everything in every way. My second, almost instantaneous, reaction was a sudden feeling of relief. If I know what I am, and as Popeye said, "I yam what I yam," I can stop striving to be something I am not. It would make life much less complicated and much more comfortable. Furthermore, I could stop struggling to make other people over into something they are not now nor ever will be.

Through extensive research and testing (20,000 people on five continents), Kolbe has identified four mutually exclusive modes over which your conative power is spread: Fact Finder, Follow Thru, Quick Start, and Implementor. She assigns the total number of mental energy units at 20 and no one has tested higher than 10 units or 50 percent in any one area.

Thanks to Kathy Kolbe for granting permission to describe her work with conation and to publish my test results. If you or your organization would like more information, please contact **Kolbe Concepts, Inc. in Phoenix, Arizona. Certified consultants are available nationwide.*

Remember, as you read these descriptions, you are not *one* of these. You are *all* of these. However, the intensity varies. For example, if you test 0-3 units in an area, you would be described as "resistant." At the other extreme, 7-10 units you would be called "insistent." "Accommodating" is used to describe those testing between 4-6 units.

FACT FINDER is the part of you that is precise, judicious, and thorough. The part of you that loves facts, detail, evidence, history, perspective, and complexity.

FOLLOW THRU is the part of you that is systematic, methodical, efficient, and orderly. The part you use to provide continuity, to pace yourself, and to put things in proper sequence.

QUICK START is the part of you that has an affinity for risk, that thrives on deadlines, crisis, challenge, and change. The part that is spontaneous, fluent, flexible, and intuitive.

IMPLEMENTOR is the part of you that deals with the tangible, the concrete. The part that is hands-on, can-do oriented.

The degree of intensity in each mode is very important. If you are **resistant** in a particular mode, yet your job requires the use of this mode, you will feel extreme stress and will soon burn out. You need to find ways around having to use this mode because you will never excel in this area. You would be well advised to delegate, team up with, hire, or marry someone who is insistent in an area where you are resistant.

If you are **insistent** in an area, and your job requires that you use this mode, you are likely to become a superstar. This is where you will shine. It is where you need to concentrate your effort.

Finally, if you are **accommodating** in a mode, you can use it as needed. You won't feel undue stress but you won't excel either.

Kolbe says one way to uncover your most insistent or resistant modes is to examine when your stress level begins to rise. For example, whenever you are blocked or prohibited from using an insistent mode, stress will escalate. An Insistent Fact Finder will be stressed when there is a lack of information, specifics, facts, or clarification. For an Insistent Follow Through too many unfinished projects, lack of closure, not enough routine, structure, or predictability causes stress. Insistent Quick Starts hate being held back, being unable to take risks, act adventurously, or intuitively. Insistent Implementors feel stressed when they don't have high quality tools or worse yet, when they have to lend their tools to people who don't appreciate them and lose or break them.

Similarly, whenever you are forced to use a mode in which you are resistant, your stress level will shoot up. For example, a Resistant Fact Finder who has to cite chapter and verse, justify actions, establish priorities, or do thing s in great detail will feel stressed. A Resistant Follow Thru hates to stay within rules, regulations, policies, or procedures. Trying to get a Resistent Follow Thru to plan ahead? Forget it! A Resistant Quick Start would rather die than have to play hunches, ad lib, or act spontaneously. And, if you want to see a Resistant Implementor's blood pressure rise, ask her to build or repair something.

FACT FINDER	**FOLLOW THRU**	**QUICK START**	**IMPLEMENTOR**
evaluate, probe,	arrange, translate,	deviate, intuit	craft, construct,
calculate, define	translate, budget	promote, invent	master, build,
prove, inquire	structure, design	brainstorm,	repair, display,
justify, research	schedule, prepare	originate, change	mold, practice,
formalize,	guarantee, chart,	challenge,	render, shape,
deliberate,	plan, format,	contrive, risk,	form,
specify, allocate,	integrate,	devise, ad lib,	use physical
investigate,	consolidate,	abbreviate,	effort,
differentiate,	provide service,	play hunches,	demonstrate,
prioritize	coordinate	experiment	put together
TO REDUCE STRESS, YOU NEED FREEDOM TO ACT ...			
correctly, thoroughly,	*consistently,*	*fluently, decisively,*	*skillfully, tangibly,*
prudently, tactfully,	*systematically,*	*rapidly, flexibly,*	*strudily, technically,*
strategically,	*fashionably,*	*intuitively,*	*mechanically,*
expertly, studiously,	*effeciently,*	*insightfully,*	*strenuously, handily,*
discerningly,	*dependably, routinely,*	*spontaneously,*	*dexterously,*
practically,	*concisely, cautiously,*	*adventurously,*	*athletically,*
deliberately,	*methodically,*	*imaginatively,*	*physically,*
conclusively,	*comprehensively,*	*defiantly,*	*demonstrably,*
appropriately	*theoretically,*	*conceptually,*	*substantively*
	continuously,	*inventively*	

Pretend for a moment that you have won the biggest lottery jackpot in history. You are filthy rich. You no longer have to work for a living but you do have to work for your mental health. What would you most enjoy doing? Which set of words best describe activities in which you'd prefer to spend your time?

(See box on previous page.)

Even after this brief discussion, you probably have an inkling of where you are most insistent and most resistant. After reading Kolbe's book you will have a solid idea of where you stand. But if you are more curious than most, there is a fun 36-item test at the back of the book. For $49.95 you can get your actual scores.

I couldn't resist. I sent it in. This was my result:

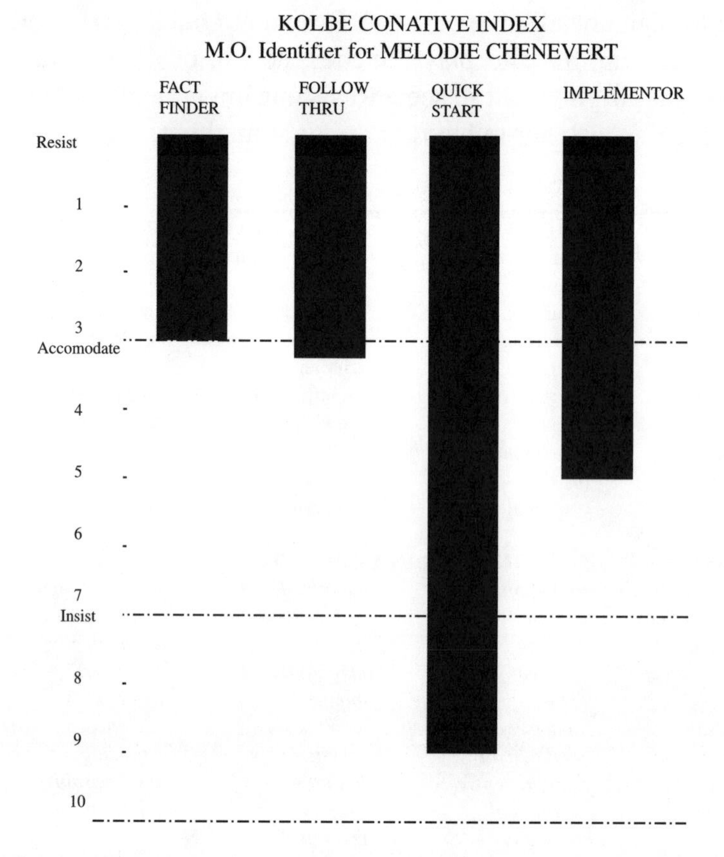

KOLBE CONATIVE INDEX

Explanation for MELODIE CHENEVERT

With your insistence as a Quick Start, you will be most productive when you:

innovate invent devise risk improvise
initiate brainstorm challenge change play
hunches promote originate contrive reform
experiment

As an insistent Quick Start, your success requires avoiding activities done:

without options	with many directions
from memory	with too many restrictions
by the book	without room for innovation
by concensus	with pre-established methods
without flexibility	while closely supervised

The effective use of your accommodating Modes of Implementor mean utilizing your ability to function:

skillfully	technically	handily
physically	tangibly	mechanically
dexterously	demonstrably	sturdily
strenuously	athletically	

Resistances for you are the Fact Finder and Follow Thru Modes, which include having to tackle tasks:

by researching	in an appropriate way
by justifying	through debate with others
with approval	by being specific
with formality	then proving you're right
with a structure	by designing a system
with a routine	by following guidelines
with precision	by making a plan
with efficiency	by being tidy

Everyone has at least 5% of each Mode, with talent in all four Modes. You can't be boxed in as all of one 'type'.

15% FF	15% FT	45% QS	25% I

As you can see, this book is being written by a Quick Start/ Implementor who is resistant in Fact Finder and Follow Thru. Remember, conation is not about what you **can** and **can't** do, it is about what you **will** and **won't** do.

When Kolbe said a Resistant Fact Finder would own a computer but never read the manual, I thought,"That's me!" My husband, Gary, is a physicist, a Fact Finder if there ever was one. He studies the manual. I just keep saying,"Show me which buttons to push." I can accomplish a lot with my computer until a glitch occurs and then I am dead in the water, I have to wait for Gary to come home and show me which buttons to push to fix it.

Gary knows I am smart and couldn't understand why I didn't study the manual. I didn't know why either. I thought I was intellectually lazy. Now I know I am just *resistant.* I have so few units available in fact finder that I have to "spend" them carefully for higher priority tasks than mastering the computer manual.

Even though I am a Resistant Fact Finder, I have two master's degrees. Amazing! I can disguise myself as a Fact Finder and pass among them but it causes enormous stress. My husband vividly remembers a day during my second stint in graduate school when I came home and announced, "If I stay in school one more term, they will beat every ounce of creativity out of me!"

Like all masters-prepared nurses teaching at the university level, I was under a lot of pressure to get my Ph.D. Val Prock, a wonderful character, was Dean of the University of Wisconsin School of Nursing at the time. I would argue with her saying, "Val, do you honestly believe I am going through all the expense, blood, sweat, and tears to get my doctorate just to tread water? Just so I can continue teaching senior students their clinical rotation in psych?"

I argued that I shouldn't do research because I am sloppy and have a short attention span. I argued that I have excellent writing skills and should be teamed up with a nurse researcher. And that both of us should be teamed up with a *real* nurse working in the trenches. But my arguments fell on deaf ears.

Today I could argue my case more convincingly. In fact, one of the things I appreciate most about Kolbe's work is that it gives me a language with which I can communicate with Fact Finders.

I am also a Resistant Follow Thru. My peculiar theory is that if I have enough drawers, I will be organized. So I collect drawers. Unfortunately, it doesn't help because they are all "miscellaneous" and most of my stuff is stacked in piles on top of them. I bought a greeting card that said, "Life is difficult for the organizationally impaired." I can't find it. It's in a pile somewhere.

That's why I said time management experts will never go hungry. Every two or three years all of us Resistant Follow Thrus sign up for a course on how to get organized. We know the suggestions given make good sense; we just don't have enough Follow Thru to consistently implement them.

There is nothing wrong with being a Fact Finder, a Follow Thru, a Quick Start, or an Implementor. Saying,"My name is Sally and I'm a Fact Finder" is not like saying ,"My name is Sally and I'm an alcoholic."

Being insistent or resistant in an area has nothing to do with good or bad or right or wrong. It has to do with differences. Take another look at the action words which describe each mode. They are all perfectly fine words. Instead of trying to iron out our differences, we need to reshape and capitalize on them.

During the break at that Denver management seminar, a participant thanked me, saying, "If I learned nothing else, it was worth coming just for the idea of conation. It makes so much sense." She continued by telling me she is charge of a clinic. Because she's a Quick Start, her favorite times are when the doctors are out and she is really in charge. She thrives on making command decisions.

A nurse working for her is a Follow Thru. She frets and worries about making decisions without proper authority. She feels any doctor is better than no doctor.

At the end of the day when the manager's ready to close things down, her Follow Thru colleague is fussing about, tidying up, and alphabetizing. She can't comfortably leave when any task is left undone. The Quick Start manager says, "Tomorrow is another day while her Follow Thru co-worker says, "Never put off till tomorrow what you can do today." They drive each other crazy.

Now the manager knows why. She also knows neither is going to change and if they can respect and work with each other's insistent and resistant modes, they can be a happy and productive team.

My favorite teacher from my diploma program actually got her master's degree after I did and then continued on to get her doctorate. During her course of study she developed Lupus. Another classmate of hers developed malignant hypertension, another was diagnosed with breast cancer, and so on. Listening to the litany of disease I said, "I'm no researcher but there is something here we should be looking at. It tells me one of two things. Either only sick people pursue their Ph.D. **or** the stress of graduate school is so intense it is making people sick."

I think it is the latter. Kolbe says all teachers from junior high on are Fact Finder Insistent. It's not malicious. It's just that a system *designed for* and *controlled by* Fact Finders is not a user-friendly place for nurses who are insistent in Follow Thru, Quick Start, or Implementor. It is not healthy.

Recently I spent an hour explaining conation to 400 nursing faculty members at a national conference. At the end of the session, a woman came up to me, shook my hand and said, "After my third hospitalization, I finally dropped out of the doctoral program."

Many nurses back in school grit their teeth, keep a low profile, and mechanically jump through the hoops, hoping after graduation they can drop the pretense and get on with what is important to them.

And think about how many times you've heard a nursing professor say something like, "if the students know the theories, if they understand the concepts, it will come out of their fingers," And how many times have you thought, "That's a crock!" Knowing something intellectually does not mean you can implement it manually.

Think about how many years we worshipped care plans. In the early 1990's Joint Commission dropped them from their requirements. Why? Because while they sounded good in theory, they did not work in the real world.

What would the ideal nurse be? A 5-5-5-5 with a turbo charger. So whenever she needed more fact finding or quick start ability she could get a power boost. It doesn't work that way. And no amount of education, or training, or will power is going to change that.

What would the ideal nursing faulty member be? A 10-10-10-10. They are harder on themselves than they are on us. Faculty are expected to do original research, publish or perish, keep clinical skills current, excel at teaching, chair committees, perform community service, provide outstanding leadership, ad infinitum.

Instead of expecting every nurse to be able to do everything, it is time we formed super teams based on conation. Nursing could rule the health care world of we would take a Fact Finder, a Follow Thru, a Quick Start, and an Implementor and team them up with a Facilitator.

Yes, there is a person who is almost 5-5-5-5. A Facilitator is a person who tests in the accommodating range in all modes. Kolbe says only 15% of the population fits this category and they are worth their weight in gold. They have the ability to understand all sides of a issue without taking one, to do things simply because they need to be done, and to keep prima donnas on task and on target.

After describing conation to a hospital-wide management group, I asked if anyone had an example that fit the theory. An administrator told of a terrible tragedy when a young doctor, a pediatric resident, vanished without a trace and was never found. He commented on how closely the actions of her fellow residents followed the conative modes. The Quick Starts brainstormed. They were full of ideas to help solve the mystery and increase future safety. However, they did not actually **do** anything about their ideas. The Follow Thrus took the Quick Starts' ideas and ran with them. They had the locks changed.

They wrote and produced a missing person flyer. The Implementors then stapled 30,000 flyers all over the city while the Fact Finders combed the medical records of every person the residence had treated in the last six months searching for clues. It was an incredible team effort.

While the theory of conation has all sorts of exciting possibilities, the focus of this book is career planning. It's taken me 30 years of constant struggle to synthesize all my talents and arrive at the perfect niche for my knack. I can't help but wonder if conation could have eliminated many painful years of trial and error.

I no longer practice nursing in the classical sense but it remains the hub of my professional life. Today I am a writer, a teacher, and an entrepreneur, but it all revolves around being a nurse.

Here's how my happy ending began. It began at the University of Wisconsin where I finally succumbed to pressure to continue my education. I enrolled in a predoctoral program majoring in Educational Psychology and minoring in Journalism. Educational Psychology was for "them." Journalism was for me. I had wanted to be a writer even in high school.

At the time my life was jam-packed. I was a full-time graduate student, half-time faculty member, wife, mother of two young sons, an aspiring artist, and a few other things. There was never an idle moment.

One day I dashed into the school of nursing office between classes to pick up my messages. A placard on the desk announced the Mosby Publishing Company representative was on campus. I asked the secretary where the Mosby man would be and a deep voice said, "I'm here." I turned to see a tall, dark, handsome man dressed like someone out of *Gentlemen's Quarterly*. My mouth dropped open. (In any school of nursing men are as rare as hen's teeth and on our campus the snappiest dressers wore new Oshkosh overalls.)

I followed him. So did half the faculty. Most of us were hoping to get a free book.

I never got a free book. I never heard the end of his sales pitch because I had to go to statistics class. But before I left I asked, "If a person had an idea for a book, what would the next step be?" He whipped our his business card and said, "Can you get me an outline by this afternoon?"

"No," I laughed. He continued, "Write an outline, a sample chapter, describe the target audience, and send it to me at this address." I raced to statistics class clutching his card in my hand.

This was my second term in statistics and I knew I was in trouble. While I had received an "A-B+" the first term, my professor had been wooed and won by the University of Texas. Our group had been divided and dumped into other classes.

My new professor was into choral recitation. He would sprawl formulas across the blackboard saying, "Da-Dum-Da-Dum-Da-Dum" and the whole class would sing back, "Dum-Ditty-Dum-Ditty-Doo." I hadn't the foggiest idea of what I was supposed to sing.

The moment I sat down he began sprawling and singing. I sat there staring at the Mosby man's card. Then I asked myself, "Do you want to be a writer or a researcher?" The answer was, "I want to be a writer."

I left the statistics class and never went back. I went to administration and reversed my course of study majoring in Journalism and minoring in Educational Psychology. I quit with a second masters in Journalism. In fact, my first book, **STAT: Special Techniques in Assertiveness Training for Women in the Health Professions,** was essentially my thesis. That book is now it its fourth edition and has been translated into French and Japanese.

The rest is history. This is my fifth book (if you count the coloring book). Deciding to become a writer was the best decision I have ever made.

Val Prock was right. Without a doctorate I can no longer teach at the university level, but I am still a teacher. Today I conduct workshops and seminars literally around the world, from America to Australia. It is fantastic. I couldn't be happier.

I want you to be as happy in your work as I am. So if you feel like a square peg in a round hole, take a long look at conation. It will help you not only understand your current discomfort, it will help you uncover your knack so you can find the right niche in nursing for you.

Oh, before I forget, I also told you conation explained why I didn't have a garage. Returning from the Denver workshop, having read Kolbe's entire book, I excitedly told my husband, "I know why we don't have a garage!"

When we moved to Maryland four years earlier, we had bought a house on a corner lot with ample room to build the garage of Gary's dreams. You see, my husband is not only a fact-finding physicist, he is a certified diesel mechanic. He loves to work with engines. He collects tools.

But in all our years together, he had never had a proper garage. Upon moving to Maryland, we vowed to change that.

For four years Gary had drawn and redrawn his ideal garage on our computer. A couple of weeks before the Denver trip he had called me in to see his latest drawing. He zoomed in on a particular spot. Not only was the nut and bolt drawn in place, the tensile strength was printed on the nut and bolt! However, in four years we had not turned one shovel of dirt to build a *real* garage.

I briefly described conation and said, "Gary, look at this: I am all Quick Start/Implementor. You are all Fact Finder/ Implementor. Neither of us has a smidgen of Follow Thru! If we are ever going to have a garage, we have to hire a contractor."

Gary, being a Fact Finder, wasn't convinced. He had never heard of conation. He was looking for some other proof or validation of the theory.

But I was a believer. Kolbe had shown me the light. I pushed and prodded until we hired a contractor. Gary kept insisting, "I can build this garage." I kept replying, "I know you can. But you won't."

Before the snow fell, a garage stood in our yard. Not just a garage but a ***garage***—big enough to hold six cars and a workshop! Gary still occasionally mutters about how he could have built the garage but he has to agree it is built. It has become his second home. He loves it.

Conation might be the key to building everything from teams, to careers, to garages. It just might be the key to living and working happily every after.

What Next?

1. How would *you* define your work? Would the synonyms you'd use be positive or negative?
2. Do you feel work is *interfering with* or *enhancing* your life?
3. Read Kathy Kolbe's **The Conative Connection**.
4. Review the action words in each mode.

FACT FINDER: evaluate, probe, calculate, define, prove, inquify, justify, research, formalize, deliberate, specify, allocate, investigate, differentiate, prioritize

FOLLOW THRU: arrange, translate, budget, structure, design, schedule, prepare, guarantee, chart, plan, format, integrate, consolidate, provide service, coordinate

QUICK START: deviate, intuit, promote, invent, brainstorm, originate, change, challenge, contrive, risk, devise, ad lib, abbreviate, play hunches, experiment

IMPLEMENTOR: craft, construct, master, build, repair, display, mold, practice, render, shape, form, use physical effort, demonstrate, put together

In which mode do you think you are most insistent?

Which best describes the actions your current job requires?

Do they match?

5. List three ways you can do more of what you love to do (and less of what you hate to do) in your current job:

A.____________________________________

B.____________________________________

C.____________________________________

6. List three jobs in nursing that might provide more of a "niche for your knack":

A.____________________________________

B.____________________________________

C.____________________________________

FOR RICHER, FOR POORER...

When I overheard a woman advising her daughter to go into nursing **for the money**, it caught me by surprise. I smiled. Not because I thought she was in error, but because most nurses would have burst into laughter. They would have told her she was crazy.

Each year I see thousands of nurses in workshops. In those focusing on professional success, I often ask participants to come up with three convincing reasons why any young person today should consider a career in nursing.

The last thing to be mentioned is money. In fact when I ask what they would reply to a teenager asking about how much nurses make, I get some pathetic answers like:

"Better than minimum wage."

"Not enough!!!"

""Our salaries are improving...ah...I think."

Nurses constantly whine about their salaries. I have not yet met a nurse who thinks she is being adequately paid. Nurses have had it drummed into their heads for so long that they are underpaid, that even dramatic evidence to the contrary does not register.

A nurse returning to the profession after a three-year absence was amazed by the sharp increase in salaries. Her colleagues seemed puzzled by her enthusiasm. They took their present salaries for granted and were disgruntled that they weren't earning more.

When a workshop group was discussing salaries, one nurse commented that ours match those of beginning engineers. The room exploded in disbelief. "No way!" bellowed a nurse in the back of the room. But it was true. Her daughter, the new graduate nurse, and her son-in-law, the new graduate engineer, were both starting at $26,000 a year.

Actually, the 1995 national average for starting salaries in nursing topped $30,000. Beginning salaries in nursing are indeed excellent.

Yet most nurses still feel they have the short end of the stick. And it they can't prove it one way, they will prove it another. For example, nurses with two years of education compare their salaries to physicians with twelve years of education. When it is pointed out that, in addition to the educational discrepancy, physicians also have to deal horrendous overhead expenses, sky-high malpractice insurance, and round-the-clock responsibility, nurses often flip-flop. They begin comparing salaries with those of plumbers, grocery store clerks, and truck drivers. None of these comparisons is appropriate.

A more realistic comparison might be to look at other female-dominated or service occupations. Nurses seem to think if we are making $35,000 a year, everyone else must be making $70,000 a year. We are seriously out of touch with reality.

According to the Census Bureau, nursing salaries are head and shoulders above those for women in general and on par with executive/managerial women. Actually, the *individual* nurse's income matches and exceeds the average *household* income!

The 1995 Earnings Survey conducted by ***RN*** found the average nurse, working full time in acute care, made $40,900. While salaries have risen more slowly in the last couple of years (about 2%/year), our income is at an all-time high.

Nurses love to plead poverty. One VP of nursing was appalled at the way nurses were trying to wheedle money out of the medical staff for their Nurses' Day celebrations. She thought it incongruous that nurses who harped on being treated with respect as professional colleagues, would be begging for donations. Furthermore, she thought if the physicians were actually aware that the nurses on her staff made between $35,000-$55,000 a year, they would tell them to go whistle for it.

When a discussion about the image of nursing began to focus on the deplorably tacky attire worn by many nurses, one of the group grumbled, "When they pay me better, I'll dress better!" Poor Cinderella.

Staff nurses are often unaware that between overtime and differentials, they may actually to making more than their managers. Nursing faculty frequently moonlight as staff nurses, not just to keep their skills current, but to supplement their income. Educators often make less than their former students.

But facts are meaningless. Perception is reality. "Feeling" poor is more crippling "being" poor. Consider Leona Helmsley. She had millions of dollars at her disposal but acted like a Scrooge with her employees. The tabloids labeled her the "Queen of Mean." Her undoing was being just as miserly with the government. She was jailed for income tax evasion. Reportedly, she was terrified of being poor.

What would it take to make you feel "not poor?" Sometimes I ask nurses to tell me exactly what they want. How much money is enough? What is the magic number that will stop all the whining?

Very few nurses have a set amount in mind. They don't know what it will take. Their only answer is, "More."

What would it take to make *you* feel "not poor?" How much salary would you need? How much money would you need to have squirreled away in the bank? Be specific.

Annual Salary__________________

Money in the bank_______________

You've heard the saying, "It's not what you make, it's what you keep." Few of us hang on to our money.

Let me introduce you to someone who can help you keep more of your hard-earned dollars. Her name is Norma Severns. Today she is a certified financial planner but for more than 25 years she was a nurse. Here are a dozen tips from Norma:

MONEY MANAGING TIPS

1. **PAY YOURSELF FIRST**. Make sure you set aside a portion of every paycheck, no matter how small the amount. And do it first! A payroll savings plan can be very helpful, especially if you are an 'out-of-sight-out-of-mind' person. If you don't see it, you don't miss it. Just $50 each month will grow to a nest egg of $74,500 in thirty years! (That's calculated on 8 percent after-tax earnings.)

2. Have a **SPECIFIC SAVINGS GOAL** in mind. For example, special vacations, household purchases, college tuition, a retirement cottage by the sea. Systematically stick to your goal. At the year's end you will see visible results. It's exciting to be successful at saving. Each year you'll aim a bit higher.
3. **KNOW WHERE YOUR MONEY GOES**. Even if close control of your money is not an issue, try keeping an expense diary one month each quarter. This will allow you to estimate your expenses accurately. Many people are amazed to see where their money actually goes. Reviewing the records may help you identify expenses that can be lowered or eliminated. You can also redirect any money "found" this way into another area of your budget that feels too restricted. Or you can save it!
4. Everyone should have an **ALLOWANCE**. Some people call this 'walking around' money. Start with the amount that you know you'll need to meet actual out-of-pocket expenses then add a little extra for impulse purchases. This adds some flexibility to your budget. An occasional reward can help you stick to your budget for the long run.
5. **PAY OFF CREDIT CARD DEBT MONTHLY**. If you have run up quite a bill on your credit cards, make retiring the balance your first savings objective. The interest rates on these accounts is astronomical. Rates of 18-21 percent are not uncommon. Talk about loan sharks!
6. **CHECK** the amount of federal and state **TAX WITHHOLDINGS**. If you routinely receive refunds, it means you are making interest-free loans to the government. Have the correct amount deducted and place the "found" money in interest-bearing accounts of your own.
7. **BUILD UP A CASH RESERVE** equivalent to three months living expenses before considering other investments. This serves as your emergency fund so you will not have to liquidate investments to meet unexpected expenses.

8. Changing jobs? Interview your new employer as carefully about **RETIREMENT OPPORTUNITIES** as you do about salary and other benefits. Look for plans that allow early participation with 100 percent vesting in your contributions at the outset and that are portable so you will retain your investment even if you change jobs. This is especially important for a nurse who often moves in relationship to a spouse's career demands.
9. **FULLY FUND ALL RETIREMENT PLAN OPPORTUNITIES**. After you've socked away three month's living expenses, this should be your first investment priority. These are usually tax deductible as well as tax deferred and represent one of the few remaining "tax shelters." Remember the $50 a month set aside in the first tip on this list? It grew to $74,500. That same $50 in a tax-deferred account would become a whopping $113,000!
10. **BUY YOUR OWN HOME**. Owning a home is a good investment. Home mortgage interest is still fully deductible which means you will pay less in federal and state taxes.
11. **WATCH PREVAILING INTEREST RATES**. Make sure you are earning competitive rates on your cash accounts. Mutual fund money market accounts usually pay higher rates than standard bank account rates. If the rate on your mortgage loan is no longer competitive, it may be time to consider refinancing. A two-point difference between your rate and the current market rate usually means refinancing will be worthwhile assuming you intend to stay in your home a few more years.
12. **BEGIN TODAY** to activate Tips 1-11!

How Norma Severns made the transition from nursing to financial planning is an interesting story. Growing up in the 1950's, Norma saw her career options as a choice of secretary, hairdresser, teacher, librarian, or nurse. Because there were lots of nurses in her family, she decided to follow family tradition and enrolled in a hospital diploma program. Later she would spend three years at Catholic University completing her bachelor's degree.

Along the way she married, had children, and worked primarily in public health. The freedom and flexibility of that role appealed to her.

Fifteen years went by and she began to get restless. She was looking for new challenges. Nurse practitioners were a fairly recent invention. She decided to enroll in a one-year program at Johns Hopkins. For the next ten years she worked as a Nurse Practitioner.

Now twenty-five years into her nursing career, she began to get restless again. She questioned the future potential of Nurse Practitioners. It was a movement which grew out of a perceived physican shortage. Now there was a glut of physicians and a struggle was on to reclaim some of the territory formerly granted to Nurse Practitioners.

She thought about getting her master's degree but another two years would mean a total of *nine years* invested in nursing education! She didn't see much hope for a reasonable return on such an investment. It only promised "more of the same."

Inspired by a friend, a former teacher who had made a successful transition to interior design, Norma decided to explore other options. Her first thought was hospital administration. Her second, law. Her third, financial planning. (Over the years she had thoroughly enjoyed being the family financial manager.)

She began researching those three options. She decided against law because it would take too long: at least three years of being a full-time student. She dismissed hospital administration because it seemed too similar to nursing. Financial planning won.

Continuing to work as a nurse, Norma enrolled in an 18-credit program from Denver's College for Financial Planning which was being offered through George Washington University. She took one course at a time figuring she had nothing to lose (the material would always be useful personally) and everything to gain.

She absolutely loved the introductory class. The second class, however, dealt with insurance and risk management. It sounded dry and stuffy. But she loved it too! She completed six courses, covering everything from taxes to retirement to estate planning, in two years.

The time had come to leave nursing.

To become a Certified Financial Planner, Norma would need three years experience in the business world. She attended a conference for advanced financial planning, hoping to get leads on possible positions.

That's where she met Alexandra Armstrong, then president of the International Association for Financial Planning. To land a position in a renowned firm like Alexandra Armstrong Associates would be a real coup.

Norma lined up interviews with three firms saving AAA for last. She hoped to use the first two as practice interviews. After all, it had been more than ten years since she had interviewed for a job. Now she was not only changing jobs, she was changing careers!

As luck would have it, the first two interviews were postponed making the AAA interview first. Resigned to the fact that her most important interview would now be her "practice" interview, she have it her best shot. She got the job! That was eight years ago.

Today Norma attributes her success as a Financial Planner to the same qualities that made her successful as a nurse—excellent communication skills along with the ability to assess, plan, implement, and evaluate. She says both careers require high quality performance, independence, flexibility, and strong decision-making skills.

The most difficult part of the transition was learning to market herself and sell her services. She had to get comfortable with the idea that her time was worth $150 an hour instead of $15 an hour and that her knowledge was valuable and not just "common sense."

Perhaps one reason nurses feel poor is that even though our salaries have improved, our lifestyles haven't. We seem to be running harder and faster just to stay in place. There is no time to enjoy life.

During my physical exam, the doctor and I were chatting about all the stressors career women must face. (Her children are in grade school.) At one point she said, "I have learned when it comes to a choice between money and time—*take time*."

Take time. A richer lifestyle has little to do with money. It has to do with getting off the treadmill and taking time to enjoy some of life's simple pleasures:

fresh flowers on the table
skipping stones on a lake
building a snowman
watching a sunset
kneading bread
tea in a bone china cup
re-reading "The Velveteen Rabbit"
a bubble bath
crisp, cotton sheets
trying on hats in an elegant store
old family photographs
phoning a long-lost friend
one Godiva chocolate
watching "The African Queen"
crunching through piles of autumn leaves
singing along with the radio
sitting still

One of the best investments you can make is to buy time. That means designating money to pay for services you have traditionally provided your family for free—cooking, cleaning, laundry, tutoring, chauffeuring, gardening, babysitting, record keeping, ad infinitum.

At a Midwestern conference for nurse managers, the lone male participant approached the registration desk. He wondered if he should sit in on the afternoon session. It dealt with the trials and tribulations of working women and he was afraid he would feel out of place. The conference organizers encouraged him to take part. They thought he would learn a lot.

At the end of the session, there was a call for questions and comments. He stood up. He looked at 99 female nurse managers and said, "Every manager here has a job as demanding or more demanding than mine. But I can tell you this. It never once occurred to me to do my own housework." He was a bachelor but he had a housekeeper coming in every week.

Those 99 women sat in stunned silence. It had never occurred to most of them **not** to do their own housework. I'll bet a lot of housekeepers were hired the next day.

A nurse told her teenage children that she planned to hire a housekeeper to come in once a week. When she told them what it would cost, they suggested she pay them and they would do the work. All went well for a few weeks and then they began neglecting their duties. Instead of nagging, she simply hired a housekeeper and discontinued that part of their allowance. They were not happy about it but agreed they had not kept their end of the bargain. A year later the housekeeper moved away. The nurse again offered the job to the children. They snapped it up and followed through, knowing if they didn't, they would be replaced.

A richer lifestyle also means being philanthropic.

When I've asked nurses to list things they want that would improve their personal or professional lives, money and time always top the list. Then there is a wide assortment of stuff ranging from the ridiculous to the sublime: being thin, getting a degree, a live-in nanny, Porsche, diamonds, travel to exotic places, respect, adequate staff, no paperwork, a parking space, better sex...

One item that caught me by surprise at first was "time to volunteer." I thought what we did for a living was so socially significant it would meet that need.

Not so. Nurses want to be able to participate in church and/or community activities. They want to be scout leaders and room mothers. They want to serve on boards, tutor inner city kids, help the homeless, and deliver meals-on-wheels.

A richer lifestyle has to do with relationships.

Jim and Cara, a husband-wife nursing duo had very successful big-city careers in the Northeast. Their salaries were spectacular, their jobs challenging. They lived for work and in the process lost sight of each other.

It wasn't until a major snowstorm trapped them at home...alone...together, that they realized what was happening. At first it was awkward. They felt like strangers making polite conversation. But before the day was out. they remembered why they had gotten married seven years earlier. They remembered how much they enjoyed each others company. What they couldn't remember was the last time they had sat down and really talked.

Each thought the other was completely happy career-wise and hesitated to bring up their own concerns. That day they discovered both of them were weary of fighting the elements, the traffic, the grime and crime. Both were concerned about shrinking budgets and increasing demands at work. Both were sick of playing politics and fighting bureaucracy.

They decided to look for work where the living was easier. They wanted a milder climate on duty and off duty. Knowing both would need to find highly specialized positions, they targeted major cities and university communities in the south and west.

Jim spotted an opening in Texas which appeared tailor-made for him. When they told him the salary range, however, he swallowed hard. It would mean a several thousand dollar cut in pay.

The only way he would even consider being interviewed was if the hospital would also line up interviews for Cara. The hospital agreed and flew them both down. They wanted Jim so much they actually managed to find an ideal position for Cara at their competitor's hospital!

Jim and Cara were impressed with everything but the salaries. Could they take such drastic pay cuts? They began doing calculations: housing, utilities, transportation, food, taxes. Everything cost less in Texas, especially taxes. Yes, technically they would make less but their money would go farther.

Today their time also goes a lot farther. They save over an hour a day just in commuting time. Since their hospitals are only a block apart, they often drive in together and meet for lunch at least once a week. Their jobs are still challenging but the pace is slower and the pressures more manageable. They say they have never felt richer.

What Next?

1. If career planning is to be reality based, the question is not: "Where can more money be made?" The question is: "Where can **you** make more money?" Given your interests, talents, education, and background. Given your geographic restrictions, family encumbrances, and present commitments. Given the state of the economy and the current job market.
2. How does your income compare with national averages for women in general, women in professional/managerial roles, and for entire households?
3. Check off which of Norma Severn's Money Managing Tips you already practice:

_____ Pay yourself first.
_____Have a specific savings goal.
_____Know exactly where your money goes.
_____Have an allowance plus some 'walking around' money.
_____Pay off credit card debt monthly.
_____Make sure federal and state tax withholdings match and don't exceed your actual taxes.
_____Have a cash reserve equal to three-months living expenses.
_____Consider retirement benefits as carefully as salary when you change jobs.

____Fully fund all available retirement plan opportunities.
____Own your own home.
____Monitor prevailing interest rates to make sure yours are competitive.

4. List three career alternatives, other than nursing, that appeal to you:
   ____
   ____
   ____

5. Research those career alternatives and see if one wins out over nursing. This may mean time in the public library, having lunch with someone already in that occupation and pumping them for information, a field trip, or volunteering in some capacity so you can see the inner workings of that profession.
6. If you are serious about a complete career change, design a workable plan to get where you want to go and be sure to include an estimated time of arrival. You may want to follow Norma's lead. Take one course at a time and gradually ease into the new profession.
7. If you want to make more money in nursing, make sure your knowledge and skills are state-of-the-art. Learn to market yourself and your services. Be willing to move, even if it is just within the same hospital. Dress professionally. Take every opportunity to promote nurses and nursing.

8. If you decide you really aren't poor, you just feel poor, ask yourself what would make your lifestyle richer. More time for life's's simple pleasures? Less housework? Involvement in a favorite cause or charity? Improved relationships? Take action to get what you need to enjoy life at home and at work.

SINGLES SCENE

Nurses love to hate their jobs. But if you think it's tough living with one, just try living without one.

Late in the evening I received a frantic call from a nurse whose whole department had been wiped out with the stroke of a pen. For weeks the hospital kept the displaced nurse at bay promising to find a slot for her. That day she had received their offer. She was shocked.

First, it was only a part-time position. Second, the schedule was so erratic it made taking on another part-time job virtually impossible. The hospital had given her 48 hours to "take it or leave it."

Single and living in an obscenely expensive metropolitan area, she was having a full-blown panic attack. A physician we both knew had suggested she call me.

She had a million questions and no answers. Should she take the job? Should she seek legal recourse? Why hadn't she seen it coming? What should she do? Should she move? Why hadn't she continued her education? Was it time to get out of nursing?

Another facility had offered her a "full-time" position on a project that would only last four months. There was a possibility it could go beyond that, but even if it did, she wasn't sure that would be what she wanted to do.

Like most of us, she was "one paycheck away from poverty." She couldn't afford the luxury of unemployment.

As I listened to her painful dilemma, I wished I had easy answers. Unfortunately, there are none. The answers are difficult to come by and unique to every nurse who finds herself in this unfamiliar situation.

I encouraged her to conserve her energy. I guided her to some reading I thought would help. I suggested just bringing up the question of legal recourse might be enough to get the hospital to give her a better severance package and access to outplacement services.

If she decided to take the short-term project, I urged her to remember her "real" job was to work through all the questions she had just asked. She should use those four months to re-evaluate her career, reconsider her location, review all her options, and to seek more permanent employment.

This was not a comfortable conversation. I'm not used to counseling unemployed nurses. I'm used to counseling *underemployed* nurses who are seeking more job satisfaction and more personal fulfillment. But satisfaction and fulfillment quickly become trivial when nurses find they can no longer provide food, clothing, or shelter for themselves or their families.

It is a crisis. It is time to hit the panic button.

We should have seen the crash coming. It hit Canada first. Shortly after nurses in the Toronto area won a handsome contract, jobs began disappearing. In fact, it seemed like it took only moments for *thousands* of nursing jobs to disappear in that metropolitan area alone. Stunned nurses found themselves joining the ranks of the unemployed. New graduates found it impossible to get positions and some felt lucky to work one shift a week. One Canadian school of nursing reported that 60 of their 90 graduates had gone south of the border and taken jobs in the United States.

But jobs for nurses in the U.S. were also drying up and blowing away. City after city announced it was saturated. Jobs were no longer going begging for nurses. Nurses were going begging for jobs.

Perhaps it shouldn't have caught us by surprise but it did. It always does.

For many decades there was a nurse shortage. Any nurse willing and able to work had a job. Then in the early 1980s the economy took a downturn. Many nurses lost their jobs and had difficulty finding another.

It was a shock to the system. Fortunately, it was short-lived.

As the economy recovered, the nurse shortage resurfaced with a vengeance. Salaries shot up. Fringe benefits and quality of work-life issues became recruitment and retention tools as hospitals scrambled to attract and hold good nurses in sufficient numbers.

Nurses quickly became spoiled. Complacent. We dozed off. We weren't paying attention to the global economic downturn sneaking up on us.

The recession of the early 1990s again caught us by surprise. The nurse shortage quickly disappeared as nurses clung to their jobs or returned to staff positions, eager to replace their spouses' lost income and fringe benefits.

What next?

If the economy recovers, we will probably be plunged into another severe nurse shortage. Why? Because all of the numbers are in place. We are an aging population. Just look in the mirror. Enormous segments of the population will soon be wearing out, breaking down, and needing care. Nurses *should* be in great demand.

That's the best case scenario. Of course if the economy doesn't recover ... *it's every nurse for herself!* And, there is growing evidence that even if the economy recovers, nursing may not bounce back as quickly or as vigorously from the current economic downturn as it did from the previous one.

We read the headlines with alarm as every industry continues to slash jobs. Not just menial jobs but professional, technical, scientific, and managerial jobs! When the Secretary of Labor talks about job retraining programs, I can't for the life of me figure out what he means. Training whom for what?

Quarterly economic statistics tell us how many jobs were lost and how many jobs were created. But since real income has been steadily declining over the last few years, I can only assume that while good jobs are being lost, the jobs being created are not so good.

As nursing jobs shift from acute care settings to long-term care and home health, we can also expect a shift in salaries. Traditionally, salaries in those areas have been considerably lower than those in acute care.

Since none of us can accurately predict the future, this book is designed to help you get a job in good times or in bad. More importantly, if you can't find a *job*, this book will help you find *work*.

WHAT DO NURSES WANT?

I remember hearing a management consultant once discussing what workers want. He began by describing workers of the past saying they essentially wanted safety, security, precise job descriptions, uniform pay increases, and a well-defined career path. I sat there shaking my head sadly and thinking that nurses are workers of the past.

Then he began describing what workers of the present and future want. Things like a piece of the action, exciting work, opportunities for intrapreneuring (doing entrepreneurial things *within* the organization), respect for their lifestyles, and how impatient they were and would continue to be.

I looked at the two lists:

PAST	***PRESENT/FUTURE***
Safety	A piece of the action
Security	Exciting work
Precise job descriptions	Intrapreneuring
Uniform pay increases	Lifestyle
Well-defined career path	Impatient!

That's when it hit me. Nurses are not workers of the past. Nurses want it all!

We want all the stability and predictability of Column One and all the fun and fulfillment of Column Two. What nurses don't seem to realize is that they are mutually exclusive. You can't have both.

Like willing prisoners, nurses have been doing time in Column One where the "system" provided everything nurses of the past wanted. It was stultifying but it was safe.

From the safety of their cells nurses looked longingly at Column Two. They envied nurses who escaped the system but even when they discovered their cell doors weren't locked, the vast majority of nurses remained in Column One. They complained but they wouldn't leave. They were afraid to let go of the old ball and chain.

Now the unthinkable has happened. The system has failed. Column One is no longer an option. You can take a pen and mark a big red X through it.

By the mid-1990s, the hallmark of our profession—job security—was gone. Those jobs we loved to hate disappeared right before our eyes. The profession we kept threatening to leave left us.

Vulnerable and confused, nurses are struggling to regain our sense of security. But no one is quite sure where security is to be found. When we look to our traditional leaders, we get mixed messages.

Our union, the American Nurses Association, is redoubling its efforts to organize us. Unions outside of our profession are also actively trying to lure frightened nurses into their ranks. Over the last few years all unions have seen their revenues diminish precipitously and they look upon two million nurses as a great way to make money.

Unions promise to take us back to the good old days. Back to Column One. A place, mind you, that no longer exists.

Our intelligentsia, on the other hand, exhorts us to invest in more education. That's their key to security. They want us to set aside our blue-collar past and move toward a white-collar future. Don't get more militant, get more scientific. Be professional.

Over the years, universities have seen their revenues diminish precipitously. They also view two million nurses as a great way to make money.

Which way should nursing go? Well, it's not so much a question of either/or as it is of neither/nor. The old ways don't work. They have failed right along with the system.

For years nurses angrily pointed out how blue-collar wages often exceeded our own. We demanded to be compensated at least as well as grocery store checkers, truck drivers, and welders. We began to emulate them. Our demands were met. We road the blue-collar train to the top of the heap and, if we don't get off right now, we're going to be riding the same train back down to the bottom.

If you want to keep up-to-date, don't read a nursing journal. It's at least a year behind. Nursing textbooks are even farther behind. Instead, pick up a newspaper.

On December 5, 1994, *The Washington Post* business section had an article titled, "Survival of the Fittest." Staff writer Peter Behr describes a woman who has worked thirty years as a seamstress for London Fog. Fifteen years ago she was making $15 an hour. Today she makes $5 an hour and is desperately trying to hold on to her job because she feels she has no other options.

What happened to the seamstress is what's happening to blue-collar workers across the board. It is generally agreed that the last good-paying blue-collar jobs were in the aerospace and defense industries. Most of those jobs are gone. Blue-collar wages have plummeted. And, if nurses persist on their present path, we could see our wages plummet too.

Does this mean nurses should jump on the nerd train? Should we emulate educators, scientists, and researchers? Again, check the newspaper.

Just a couple of weeks later, on Christmas Day, 1994, *The Washington Post* began an in-depth series of articles titled, "American Science: Losing Its Cutting Edge?"

Not only is your common laborer in trouble, just look at what's happening to your common scientist. According to staff writer Boyce Rensberger, a brand new scientist with a PhD can expect a starting salary of $18,000 to $20,000 a year! (Brand new nurses, take note.)

Instead of spending their days pursuing pure research, scientists are forced to spend a significant portion of their days begging for bucks. Many scientists are on "soft money" meaning they have to hustle for grants to pay their salaries and support their research. The competition for dollars is intense because while the number of scientists has burgeoned, funding has remained flat. More and more are competing for less and less. (Nurse researchers, take note.)

Like migrant workers, many scientists are forced to shuffle from lab to lab because they can't find permanent jobs. Many middle-aged, mid-career scientists are still "temping" and making less than $25,000 a year. Today bright young people are being steered away from careers in science because the job market is so bad and is not expected to improved in the foreseeable future. (Nurse educators, take note.)

Blue-collar workers can't find jobs.
White-collar workers can't find jobs.
Where are all the jobs???

New Yorkers joke about reading the obituaries to find an apartment. With jobs becoming equally scarce, I wonder if we might see the obituaries eventually merge with the help-wanted ads.

"Betty Berkowitz died today leaving a husband, two cats, and a night nurse position open on the orthopedic unit at Our Lord Have Mercy Hospital."

But it probably won't happen because whether we die, retire, move, or get fired, we no longer leave "openings." The job disappears too. No replacement is sought. In fact, some experts think we are witnessing the demise of the job.

When hospitals struggle to survive by closing beds, combining units, reducing departments, consolidating services, drastically down-sizing or merging, nurses get caught in the crunch.

If you find yourself without a job, the "victim" of a hospital merger or down-sizing, you may feel like a casualty of war. Dead and gone. This was not supposed to happen. Perpetual job security has been an unwritten law in nursing.

If you find yourself a "survivor" of a hospital merger or downsizing, you may still feel like a victim. At first you will feel relieved to have survived the cut. You may even feel guilty because you have a job and some of your colleagues don't. After the guilt comes anger, then depression. Who knows? Your job may be eliminated tomorrow. These emotions are normal. They correspond closely to the stages of grieving with which you are so familiar. You just might not have realized the loss of a job (or threatened loss) could effect you almost as deeply as the loss of a spouse or family member.

In these turbulent times it makes good sense to look out for your own professional good. Your first loyalty should be to yourself. Don't expect the hospital to take care of you. Most hospitals can barely take care of themselves. They cannot promise you a job forever.

Job security is a thing of the past. The only security lies in making sure you are employable. That means doing anything you can to maintain and increase your skills. That means improving your credentials and building a solid reputation.

While a nurse may say she has had twenty years of experience, she may actually have only one year of experience which she has repeated for the last twenty years. If your specialty unit closed today, where else would you be qualified to work? This makes a great case for cross-training.

Expand your area of expertise. Ask for new challenges. Request assignments in another specialty area. When you are asked to float to an unfamiliar floor, look on it as an opportunity to gather information. You can get a glimpse of what it might be like to be an orthopedic nurse instead of a coronary care nurse. Attend in-service programs, college classes, or concurrent sessions at conventions that help get you out of your comfortable rut. Read books or journal articles related to other fields. Stretch. Grow.

If you find yourself detached from you job by choice or by chance, in good times or in bad, you may feel a lot like a person who has been divorced or widowed. Whatever the emotional or economic climate, sooner or later you have to get back in circulation.

So, just where do you go to meet a nice job?

Looking in the classified ads can be a lot like going to a singles bar. Both parties may be desperate. The institution doing the advertising may feel any nurse is better than no nurse. The nurse reading the ads may feel any job is better than no job.

If your self-esteem is low, you may respond to the first hospital that even winks in your direction. You may impulsively grab the first offer that comes your way. To keep that from happening, make appointments with several hospitals and go exploring.

Pledge to complete all the interviews before making your choice. A recruiter may pressure you to accept immediately — "this offer expires at midnight!" Resist the pressure. A decision this important cannot be made on the spot.

If you are desperate and you need a job *now,* take on the new position knowing it's a shotgun wedding. It's a marriage of necessity and convenience. You may grow to love your job. If you do, that's terrific. If you don't, that's okay. Use this job to get through your financial crisis. When the pressure is off, rework your career plans.

Just as the majority of available people are not hanging out in singles bars, the majority of available jobs are not in the newspaper. In fact, your may want to check out hospitals that are conspicuous by their absence. It may mean they have a stable staff with low turnover rate.

One way to find a good job is to take an active role in your state or district nursing organizations. Volunteer to serve on a committee so that you can rub shoulders with nurses from a variety of institutions. Nurses are quite candid when discussing their employers. By keeping your eyes and ears open, you can learn a lot about the level of job satisfaction among nurses in your neighborhood. In no time you'll know which hospitals to pursue and which to avoid. Put out feelers. Tell other committee members you are thinking of re-entering nursing or making a job change. Ask for suggestions. They may have the inside scoop on positions that will open soon. They can also put you in touch with the right people to expedite things.

When you attend a convention, look at the job search board. Don't be afraid to approach a speaker who might have some information that could be helpful. Socialize. A career breakthrough could come during the fun and games.

Read the want ads in professional journals. Even if you are not interested in making a major move, those ads will help you keep current on which areas of nursing are hot and which are not.

Each year a couple of major nursing journals publish special career guides. These issues usually have a handful of articles related to career management. The bulk of space, however, is devoted to advertisements from hospitals all over the country trying to entice you to come work for them. Comparing the information in those ads is a quick way to assess what's available in terms of salary and fringe benefits. They also usually list the name of the nurse recruiter and encourage you to call toll-free or collect. So call. Talk to the recruiter. Ask for an application. In fact, ask for job applications from several hospitals. Make a list of the information most requested. Then develop a master information sheet on yourself. It will save a lot of time and effort when you actually begin making applications.

Watch for job fairs. Companies like Nursing Spectrum sponsor events where recruiters from hospitals and other organizations can hook up with nurses. To entice nurses to attend, they often provide free continuing education programs. Take your time walking through the exhibits. Browse. Don't be afraid to ask questions.

In addition to sponsoring job fairs, Nursing Spectrum publishes a full-color tabloid twice a month with articles of interest to the working nurse and lots of job opportunities. They currently target five geographic areas: Chicago, New York, Washington DC, Philadelphia, and Florida.

Hospitals, especially those in large metropolitan areas, often have an "open house." They provide tours, food, and fun. It is a good way to see what they might have to offer with no strings attached. Even if you have a job, attend. You never know when you will be looking for another job and you may stumble upon unexpected opportunity.

The American Nurses Association has a Nurse Placement Center. You may register for a nominal sum of $5 for members or $15 for nonmembers. Nursing students may register free. You simply fill out a standardized form giving a thumbnail sketch of your education, employment history, certifications, desired positions, geographic preferences, and specialties. You will receive a confidential identification number to protect your privacy. Your resume is then "summarized" and published in the "ANA Nurse Placement Center Monthly Register." That register is mailed to nurse recruiters and employers who subscribe to the service. If there is further interest, your complete resume will be made available. You are then notified if an interview is desired. You are still in the driver's seat. Your name and address have not been released. You make the decision about whether you wish to pursue the job opportunity.

Nursing specialty organizations have newsletters and journals which list jobs of interest to their members. If you are certified, experienced, or just interested in a particular area of nursing, read through their materials. Instead of approaching the personnel department, introduce yourself to the nurse managers on those units, tell them about yourself in 25 words or less, and inquire about current openings and possible future opportunities.

If you have a school of nursing in your area, you may want to check their bulletin boards for job notices. You can make an appointment with the faculty members who represent your clinical interests and pick their brains for ideas. Talk with the professor who guides senior students in career planning. You might want to sign up for an advanced nursing course just to expand your network. Alumni organizations may also provide some job placement service. Check it out.

In almost every field and discipline there seems to be a trend toward hiring "mercenaries"—professionals who come in to do a specific job, collect the cash, and then vanish. It saves the institution a lot in terms of fringe benefits and allows them to hire only the staff they need.

By going to work for a temporary agency, you can experience what it would be like working for a certain employer without making a commitment. Ask the agency for varied assignments at a number of different hospitals in your community. You might like "playing the field" and decide to take temporary assignments permanently or you might come upon a hospital or a particular unit where you would like to settle down. If that happens talk to the people in charge and visit the personnel department. Start the ball rolling.

Instead of working for an agency, you can become an agency—with a personnel list of one. There is nothing to prevent you from hiring yourself out to a hospital, an extended care facility, or to a family in need of a private duty nurse. One of my former classmates did just that. She approached it in a very businesslike fashion. She set her fees by splitting the difference between what an agency charges the hospital and what they actually pay a nurse on their roster. She then approached several directors of nursing, giving them her business card and fee schedule. It was a win-win situation. Before long she had more work then she wanted. After all, the reason she had done this in the first place was to cut back on the number of hours she was working and to gain control of her schedule. Learning to turn down assignments was one of the hardest lessons.

Another nurse worked for years in a doctor's office. When he retired and sold his practice, she decided to look for other options. She wasn't ready to retire but she did not want to work full-time. She made a flyer advertising her services as a temporary office nurse and took them to doctors within a 30 minute drive of her home. Between maternity leaves, vacations, and substituting for nurses on sick leave, she quickly found as much work as she wanted.

In this age of itinerant workers, professionals in every field are building portfolios of marketable skills and taking them to a variety of industries. If you doubt nurses will become itinerant workers, just look at the proliferation of advertisements for "flying" nurses and the fact that "rent-a-nurse" agencies continue to be multi-million dollar businesses.

In today's job market and economy, it is smart to think of cross-training in skills and abilities that may fall outside of traditional nursing.

Nurses who want to pursue higher education are often frustrated by the unavailability of nursing degree programs or by the fact that those available are grueling, cumbersome, and not geared for the adult learner.

Claudia was a director of nursing at a university hospital. She decided to get her master's degree. Because the hospital was a stone's throw from the university school of nursing, she walked over to make some inquiries. They gave her forms to fill out and assigned her to an advisor.

When they reviewed her application, they had some bad news. It seemed the diploma program she had attended some 20 years ago had long since closed and the records were incomplete. Her bachelor's degree had not included some courses which the school of nursing thought vital. They told her she would have to make up several deficits before they could consider admitting her.

Thoroughly discouraged, she was about to abandon her plans for graduate school, when a colleague suggested she go see what the school of business might have to offer. When they reviewed her application they said in effect, "WOW! You function at the director's level. You handle a zillion bucks a year! You belong in our Executive MBA Program!"

The hospital had to agree to give her release time every other Friday and she had to agree to go on her own time every other Saturday. She emerged two years later with an MBA.

Looking back she feels she was lucky the school of nursing closed the door in her face. Professionally she is much more viable and more versatile. She has no doubt her subsequent promotion to the vice president level was due to her business background, not her nursing background.

Nurses in the trenches often look up at nurses in management roles and envy their job security. Actually, the higher you climb in an organization, the less secure your job may be. Nurses who become educators, clinical specialists, managers, and executives often find their jobs pulled out from under them. A new CEO arrives, bringing his own VP for Nursing with him. Budget cutbacks may eliminate any nursing research and severely trim such departments as education and staff development. Clinical nurse specialists are often viewed as nice but nonessential personnel. Many hospitals are reducing their management level positions, with devastating effects for head nurses and supervisors.

The higher your position, the more difficult and time consuming it will be to find a comparable position. One Vice President for Nursing was give the axe so suddenly, she was in total shock. She was simply told on Friday not to be there on Monday.

When she regained her senses, she hired a lawyer who managed to get her nine months severance pay instead of three and, more important, extensive outplacement services to help her in her job search. It took nearly a year to find the right position. While this story had a happy ending, it was a miserable year that she hopes never to repeat.

When another director of nursing found herself the victim of a palace coup for the second time, she decided to make a complete career change. She returned to school and is now in private practice as a marriage counselor.

One nurse commented that she was concerned about not completing her doctorate. She said she was afraid she would limit her options. Actually, she might limit her options more by completing her doctorate. She would be considered over qualified for 90 percent of the jobs available in nursing. There are pros and cons to everything.

While losing your job is always traumatic, don't make it tragic. When Margo lost her job at the hospital, she thought it was the end of the world. A couple of days later, one of her down-sized colleagues suffered a massive stroke and died. The loss of her friend quickly put things in the proper perspective.

Margo decided losing her job wasn't the end—it was a chance for a new beginning. Instead of frantically trying to find another position, she stepped back and began looking at her entire life, not just her livelihood.

No longer panicky, she is thoroughly enjoying the process of finding work. She laughed as she told me the results of her first career apptitude tests. They suggested she seek work as a forest ranger or a social secretary. She is excited about the prospect of finding not just a new job, but possibly a whole new career.

What Next?

1. If you found yourself suddenly unemployed, how long would your cash reserves hold out? How long could you stay afloat without a regular paycheck?

2. Read the want ads in your local paper.

3. Attend an open house or a job fair.

4. Who's in your "good old nurse network" that could help you find a job?

5. What organizations do you belong to? How *active* are you?

6. List three things you are currently doing to make yourself more employable:

____

____

____

7. If you lost your job, would it be the end ...

or the beginning?

MATCHMAKING

When it comes to job hunting, nurses have been spoiled. Many have never even written a resume. They simply called to inquire about available jobs, and were offered positions over the phone, sight unseen. Others have dropped into a hospital, filled out an application form, and were asked if they could begin work that evening. As one recruiter said, "If you could fog a mirror, you were hired!"

But what do you do when "breathing" isn't enough to get you a job?

IT'S NOT WHAT YOU KNOW, IT'S WHO YOU KNOW

Let me pause for a moment and tell you about our older son, Eric. He inherited my sense of humor and my short attention span. He also inherited a double dose of brains which enabled him to to sleepwalk through high school. After graduation he shocked us by enlisting in the Marine Corps where among other things he became water-survival qualified.

When he finally got to college, he couldn't find his niche. He lacked focus. Math? Science? Engineering?

On spring break he went to Florida and became a certified scuba diver. He came home and announced he wanted to become an underwater welder.

I went ballistic. My firstborn was not going to become a welder on land or on sea. I didn't care how much they made! He was going to get a degree.

Gary, my physicist-husband, was more circumspect. He thought Eric should be allowed to go to college at his own pace, when and if he was ready. While Gary and I debated, Eric found a school he wanted to attend: Florida Institute of Technology.

At first I was afraid it might be one of those "drive-the-big-rigs" vocational schools but it turned out to be a private college with an excellent ocean engineering program. I was thrilled.

Eric did get a degree. Unfortunately, he couldn't get a job. He spent months looking for an entry-level position. No luck.

He moved home and continued his search. It was a thoroughly demoralizing experience. We all felt helpless.

Bored and bewildered, Eric finally asked if he could go to a commercial diving school. Frankly, we didn't know what else to do. So he left for a four-month course at the Ocean Corporation in Houston.

"How ironic!" I thought. "After I arm-wrestled this kid into getting his degree, he's going to end up an underwater welder after all."

I couldn't help thinking of the time and money we could have saved. My mind kept flashing back to a Far Side cartoon in which the dean is shaking hands with each new graduate at commencement and saying, "Thanks for the $86,000. Thanks for the $86,000. Thanks for the $86,000."

Two days before he finished the diving program, the president called him into his office and said, "Now, Eric, tell me exactly what it is you want to do." Eric explained that he had his degree in ocean engineering but he didn't want a desk job. He wanted to be a diver too.

With that the president asked his secretary to bring in the such-and-such folder. He picked up the phone and began dialing. He called his contacts in different companies. In fact, the whole faculty was busy making calls trying to match their students with available positions. In less than 48 hours, Eric had a great job on the underwater team of an engineering firm outside of New York City.

I'm sharing this experience with you for two reasons. One is that finding a job is more about *who* you know than *what* you know, especially in a tight job market. And second, it underscores how institutions of higher learning often fail to give their graduates any practical help in finding employment.

In Eric's case, the college took our money and said, "Lots of luck." The vocational school, however, left nothing to luck. They saw job placement as part of their mission.

Schools of nursing should do the same. The dean and the faculty must maintain connections in the real world so they can help students with job placement. Curricula must be revised to provide both job search skills and career planning information.

New and used nurses need to know how to construct a resume and how to interview to win the job. For many nurses, information in these areas is not just obsolete; it's nonexistent.

THE RESUME: YOUR PERSONAL AD CAMPAIGN

This chapter will help you put together an advertising campaign. Your goal is to sell your product: ***you***.

Have you ever sneaked a peek at the "personal ads" in your local paper? You know, the ones that read: "SWM seeking SWF for R & R PDQ." Well, your résumé should have some things in common with those personal ads. It should be ultra concise, explicit, and exciting enough to evoke a positive response.

Think of your résumé as a sixty-second commercial. That's about all the time it has to make an impression. Someone in the personnel department will give it a brief glance and deposit it in a pile designated "Yup" or "Nope" or "Well...Maybe."

That's why your résumé should not exceed **one** page. And there should be plenty of white space to make it easy on the eye! To do that you must eliminate any extraneous words or phrases. For example, do not include references. Do not use the vacuous phrase "references available on request." That is taken for granted. Do not include personal information like age, height, weight, marital status, or hobbies. Do not include your salary history. (That's like shooting yourself in the foot.)

While some experts advocate having a career-objective statement, others feel it may do more harm than good. It may serve to eliminate you from further consideration. If your résumé is going to the personnel department, do not bother with a cover letter. However, if you are bypassing personnel and going directly to the department head, use your cover letter to introduce yourself and explain why you are enclosing your résumé.

A word of caution: Even though your résumé is only one page long, it is not something you dash off. It is something you labor over.

Just as a sixty-second television commercial requires hundreds of hours behind the scenes and miles of film, your résumé will represent many hours of work. And, just as most of the film ends up on the cutting room floor, most of the work you do on your résumé won't make the final cut. That doesn't mean all the work you've done has been wasted. Going through this process makes you re-evaluate your goals and re-assess your priorities. It clarifies your desires. It helps you review your strengths and weaknesses. Best of all, it gets you ready for the interview. Think of it as a rehearsal on paper.

That's why most experts agree that you should write your own résumé and not contract it out to a résumé-writing service. You not only save money, you learn a lot about yourself in the process.

BEHIND THE SCENES

Before attempting to write a formal résumé, you need a pile of scratch paper and some thinking time. Begin your advertising campaign by reviewing your personal qualifications. What words would you, your best friend, or your boss use to describe you?

Here is a list. Circle the adjectives that apply to you. Feel free to add others that pop into your mind.

Honest	Reliable	Compassionate
Persistent	Efficient	Positive
Organized	Thorough	Loyal
Creative	Precise	Adaptable
Diplomatic	Calm	Productive
Thoughtful	Ethical	Professional
Intelligent	Outgoing	Dependable
Responsible	Caring	Flexible
Conscientious	Optimistic	Genial
Patient	Poised	Methodical
Self-motivated	Quick learner	Imaginative
Versatile	Even-tempered	Assertive

Systematic	Trustworthy	Energetic
Competent	Tenacious	Businesslike
Friendly	Practical	Analytical
Inquisitive	Problem Solver	Team player

Some less positive words may come to mind such as long-suffering, brooding, frugal, feisty, abrasive. Edit those out or put a positive spin on them. Long-suffering becomes perseverant and frugal becomes cost conscious.

ACCOMPLISHMENTS

It was Woody Allen who said that showing up is 80 percent of success. A lot of nurses think by just showing up, they've done their duty. Many have never stopped to think about what they have accomplished day in and day out.

It's time for you to stop and think about your accomplishments. It's time to make a written inventory of your work experiences.

On separate sheets of paper list each of your former employers with address, phone number, and the dates you worked there. Even if you've only had one employer, you may have worked in several areas or in many different capacities. Write down a description of what you have **accomplished** in each.

Use action words. Here's a list to help you:

Coordinated	Trained	Simplified
Collected	Counseled	Directed
Reduced	Developed	Operated
Provided	Assisted	Budgeted
Organized	Reorganized	Installed
Expanded	Identified	Taught
Planned	Maintained	Represented
Administered	Performed	Adjusted
Hired	Fired	Improved
Analyzed	Documented	Researched
Created	Merged	Obtained

Saved	Produced	Supervised
Purchased	Constructed	Designed
Led	Managed	Monitored
Reported	Controlled	Initiated
Evaluated	Inspected	Implemented
Modified	Edited	Collaborated
Decreased	Generated	Conducted
Served	Facilitated	Budgeted
Launched	Set up	Mediated
Controlled	Established	Instructed

Many of us suffer from the "just-a-nurse" complex. When the value of working in a minimum-wage, fast-food establishment was questioned by a person who didn't think "flipping hamburgers" was a marketable skill, the owner of one of those restaurants countered with this list of what a worker can learn on the job. Skills such as customer relations, meeting deadlines, keeping records, doing inventory, following regulations, making decisions, handling money, mastering new procedures, and teamwork. Good grief! If you can learn all this in a fast-food joint, just think of all you have learned in a health-care joint.

Go back through that list of action words again. Give yourself credit where credit is due.

Your résumé should also include a summary of your education. If you are very young, you can include high school. Otherwise, begin with college or vocational schools attended, the dates you were there, degrees or diplomas received. Are you certified in a specialty area? Are you cross-trained? Don't just include it, emphasize it.

Your résumé should be printed on crisp, high-quality paper, preferably white or a mild variation thereof. One-inch margins all around. Error and wrinkle-free.

Unlike the personals, however, it should not be cute. There should be no colored paper, gags or gimmicks, stars or hearts, cartoons or clip art, photos or video tape. A résumé should mean business.

Begin with the most important information:

NAME
ADDRESS
PHONE NUMBER

Then lead with your strongest selling point in light of the position you are pursuing. It may be your skills and accomplishments or it may be highlights of your work or professional experience. Education will usually be listed last.

Whatever you do, **make it easy to read.**

If you need more help in preparing your résumé, you will find dozens of books on the library shelf. Some contradict others so look for current titles and check the background of the author.

Remember, the only goal of the résumé is to get an interview and landing an interview in tough times is ... well, *tough*. View the personnel department as the front door to the organization. If you find the front door locked, go in the back door. Go right to the unit or division where you hope to work and take your résumé with you.

THE NOT-SO-BLIND-DATE

Once you land the interview, remember there will be no long courtship, You may have only one face-to-face chance to secure this match. Since an important, lucrative relationship is at stake, both parties need to do a lot of homework before the big event.

Your potential employer will have studied your résumé, verified your employment history, educational preparation, and licensure. You may even have been asked to take some pre-screening tests.

Your homework should include looking at their physical plant, reading their annual report, examining their philosophy and mission statement, and checking out their reputation. It's smart to take a look at articles about the facility in the archives of the local paper.

A lot is riding on this interview, this "first date," so get as much information as possible about how they see the ideal candidate in terms of knowledge, skills, experience, and personal attributes. Find out the scope of the position, key responsibilities, current objectives, and future projections.

In the past a hospital might have had a dozen openings and a single applicant. They took almost any nurse who applied and plugged her somewhere into their system. Today there may be a dozen applicants for a single opening. Make no mistake. This is a contest. Competition will be keen. What sets you apart?

The focus should not be on how much you need this job. The focus should be on what you can do to help the organization achieve its goals. How do your personal and professional qualifications combine to make you an excellent candidate? What makes you the solution to their problem?

Don't be surprised by a gang interview or a series of round-robin interviews. Be aware that each person who interviews you will have a different personality, a different agenda, and may even represent a different discipline. Each will be looking at how well you will fit with the team. Each will be looking at what you can bring to the party.

Expect open-ended questions about your skills, achievements, strengths, weaknesses, knowledge-base, future plans, and goals. Interviewers may ask questions directly related to their mission statement. They may ask you about ethical issues, about the way you define quality, about the way you implement customer service.

The best indication of future performance is past performance. That's why references used to be very important. Today, however, fear of litigation has caused many institutions to reduce references to no more than a verification of the dates you were employed.

So how do prospective employers get information about your past performance? They get it from you. They will either pose hypothetical situations or ask you to describe actual situations in which you:

- solved problems
- demonstrated leadership

- took risks
- collaborated with other disciplines
- enhanced teamwork
- managed a crisis
- contained costs
- handled complaints
- negotiated a settlement
- set priorities
- resolved conflict

Throughout the process, they will be looking at your poise, candor, grace under pressure, professional demeanor, attitude, and communication ability.

Other tips? Dress professionally. Smile. Maintain eye contact. Be confident. Never say a negative word about your former employer or colleagues. Don't chew gum, smoke, eat, or drink during the interview. Don't fidget, crack your knuckles, or twist your hair. Don't ask about salary or fringe benefits. That should be discussed only after you are offered the job and *before* you accept.

FINDING WORK WHEN YOU CAN'T FIND A JOB

The best place to find work after you've lost your job will surprise you. It's the organization that just laid you off!

Oh, the job may be gone but the work lingers on. Only so much can be parcelled out to the remaining staff. The rest just begins piling up.

Earlier I talked about the "survivor guilt" felt by those who still have jobs after downsizing. But one exhausted nurse manager told me survivors should feel no guilt whatsoever. According to her, those who were fired or laid off are the lucky ones! The poor stiffs who still work for the hospital are buckling under unrealistic work loads.

When someone from personnel told Lori they didn't have a job description for her, she burst into laughter. The management trainer had left, the patient advocate had left, and the hospital had decided they didn't want to pay a consultant to do re-engineering. All of these positions and projects had ended up in Lori's lap. In addition to her staff development position, she is now expected to do the work of at least three other people.

So before you bid farewell to your old employer, look around and see if you can spot some work that needs doing. You may be able to work on a per-project basis or even design a new and better position for yourself.

For example, five nurse educators were told by the hospital that their positions would be abolished in three months. If they couldn't be absorbed by other departments, they would be terminated.

I don't know what happened to the other four, but I do know what happened to Jessica. She used the time to study and do a little field research. She took a couple of business courses at the university and visited rural hospitals and outlying agencies to see what their educational needs were. Then she put together a proposal in which the hospital would market educational programs to its neighbors. The revenues would be used to support in-house education.

The administration gave her a thumbs-up. The program has been an unqualified success. What began as Jessica's worst nightmare ended up as her dream job.

IF YOU'RE NOT A GO-GETTER, YOU'RE A GONER

A couple of years ago I met a real go-getter. Her name is Connie Sikes. After she got her BSN from Texas Woman's University, she worked briefly in a very understaffed hospital and then left to teach at an associate degree nursing program. Along the way she completed her master's in Nursing and Community Health Education.

After a dozen years of teaching and overcome with frustration, she suddenly quit. It was on a Friday in December between fall and spring semesters.

That afternoon she called the nursing director of the operating room at a local hospital and told her she wanted to work in the OR but she needed to have a job immediately. That Monday morning she went to her new job and began learning her new craft. Nurses she had once taught were now teaching her.

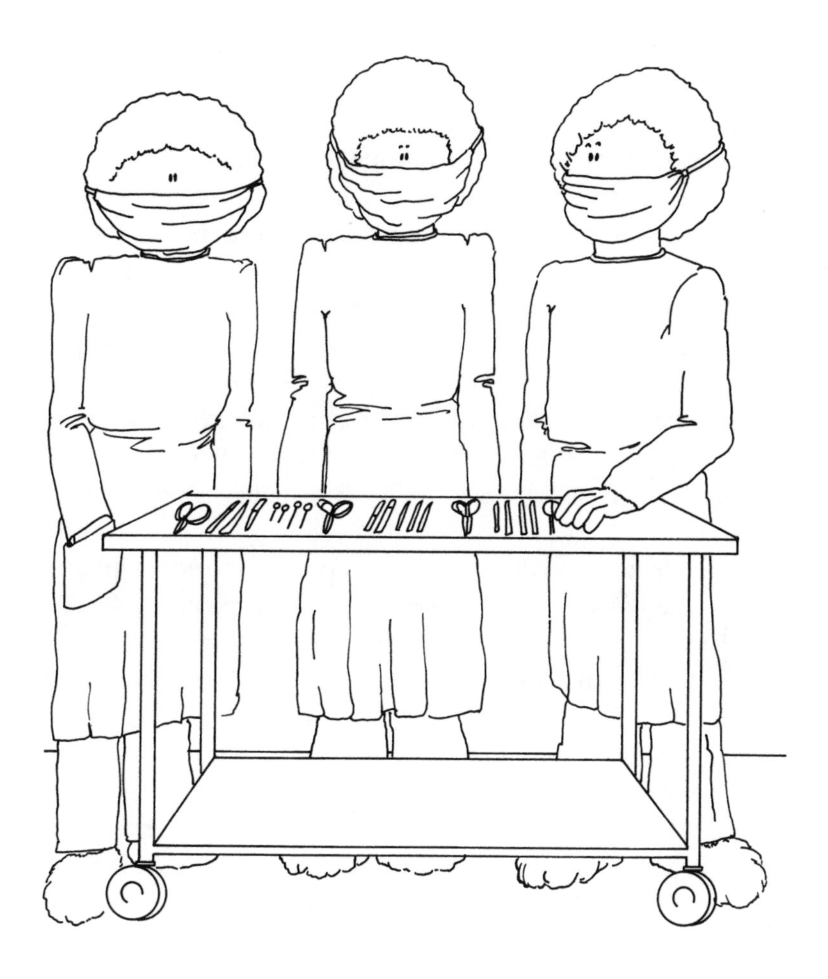

Connie developed a system to file the physicians' preference cards, a system which she says saved the hospital her salary each and every day and then some. She encouraged the nurses to go with her for OR certification. They studied together and all became certified. She organized quality assurance programs, continuing education and in-service programs.

However, when the education position became available, a nurse with more seniority got the job. That was Connie's wake-up call. After seven years in the OR, Connie realized she had developed "tunnel vision." It scared her to realize that career decisions were being made for her. She decided to swing into action.

She reviewed the JCAHO standards and wrote down questions about each hospital department. She called all the hospital vice presidents and directors and made appointments to interview them. She told them she needed to understand their areas better so she could work with them to achieve common goals.

About that time the hospital sponsored a contest titled, "Where Will the Hospital Be in the 90's?" She took the information she had gathered, identified future goals *and* how to accomplish them. She submitted it in outline form, knowing the administrator (the contest judge) had a just-the-facts personality.

She won first prize and $300! But that was only the beginning.

Connie had also described a new position to accomplish what she had envisioned. Two months later the position was developed as she had described and the qualifications for the position were taken from her résumé. Periodically, she reviews that prize-winning outline to make sure she stays on target. And she makes sure she stays highly visible.

She loves her job in administration. Actually, she says she hesitates to call it a "job" because she is having so much fun. At long last, she has the authority as well as the responsibility to make changes. She says she is able to energize and encourage her colleagues while supporting the goals of the institution.

Connie loves to tell her story to nursing students and anyone willing to listen. She sees no reason why nurses can't seize control of their careers and design jobs that they will love.

KEEP YOUR EYES OPEN FOR UNMET NEEDS

Keep your ears open too. During a break at a neonatal conference, I overheard a nurse practitioner lamenting about having to discharge a mother and baby to a homeless shelter six hours after giving birth. Another nurse volunteered her personal story about early discharge. She had a C-section and was sent home within 48 hours. Even with all her knowledge and experience (she was a lactation consultant), she was thoroughly miserable and couldn't imagine how the average mother was able to cope. Another nurse joined in detailing some horror stories about newborns returning to the hospital with grave complications. These "boomerang" babies were "contaminated" by the outside world so they couldn't return to the newborn nursery. The only option was to put them in pediatrics where they were exposed to all sorts of peril.

Setting aside the ethical, moral, and legal ramifications of this discussion, just think of the opportunities! These nurse have stumbled onto a veritable gold mine.

Can't you just picture it? A roving band of neonatal nurses and lactation consultants criss-crossing the country, providing education and support. It's not just the homeless who need this service but also affluent, well-educated people who know the value of a good start in life and are willing to pay for it. Picture videotapes and hot lines (900 numbers) for anxious parents. Picture a half-way-house nursery for "boomerang" babies. The possibilities are limited only by our imaginations.

Pick up any newspaper and you can find opportunities for nurses and nursing, not in the want ads, but in the headlines. For example, we all read about the hospital in Tampa where they amputated the wrong foot of a patient and a couple of weeks later they disconnected the respirator on the wrong patient with fatal consequences. In West Virginia a woman whose legs had been severed in a horrible head-on collision with a semi-truck spent the night in the morgue. The next morning they discovered she was still breathing. Or the journalist with breast cancer who went through the hell of a bone-marrow transplant at a world-famous facility only to die because she had received four times the recommended dose of her chemotherapy four days in a row.

Nurses could run a very legitimate protection racket. A fearful public could well demand the return of private-duty nurses to act as a first line of defense against a system more concerned with cutting costs than with patient safety.

Another example from my local newspaper: the General Accounting Office reports that nearly 5 million elderly Americans are taking unsuitable and potentially harmful drugs. Furthermore, it suggested hospitalizations from inappropriate drug use cost about $20 billion a year. Any ideas, nurses?

Need more inspiration? I just read about a "grief camp" for children who are struggling to cope with the loss of a loved one. It's Camp Jamie in Frederick County, Maryland, and its success is inspiring other communities to start their own. Does it inspire you to start anything?

Or do you get any ideas from headlines like this: "Marriott Plans Big Expansion for Senior Care Center." Another article described how difficult it is for families caring for elderly members to get away for much-needed vacations. One family was spending almost $1300 to put Grandpa in a nursing home for a week so they could go to the beach. Enterprising nurses might think about starting a respite resort so Grandpa could go to the beach too. It would make families feel a lot less guilty to park their loved ones in a resort than in a nursing home.

BOLDLY GO WHERE NO NURSE HAS GONE BEFORE

Police in New York City are twice as likely to commit suicide as they are to be killed in the line of duty. When I heard that startling statistic on the television news magazine *PRIMETIME LIVE,* I immediately thought of Colleen Knudson in St. John, New Brunswick. She was a nurse ahead of her time.

Colleen had gone to a diploma school in the New Brunswick psychiatric hospital where she still works some 22 years later. Like most nurses, she took job security for granted. It never occurred to her that she wouldn't continue to work there until retirement.

Then the economy began to go sour and sweeping changes hit the health care industry. She watch as one fellow nurse manager after another bit the dust. Where there had once been ten

managers, there were now only three. She expected a pink slip any day. The tension was palpable.

Feeling she couldn't just sit still, waiting for the budget-cutting ax to fall, she began to formulate a back-up plan. She would open her own business.

Actually, the idea to go into business had been percolating in her mind since she had returned to school to complete her bachelor's degree. In a course on crisis she had to do a class project. She wanted to do something unusual, something different and nontraditional for a nurse. She wanted to venture outside of health care and she thought it would be interesting to work with a predominately male population for a change.

Somewhere Colleen read about a "ride-along" program where you could accompany the police on their rounds. Since one of her nurse colleagues was married to the deputy chief of police, she got his permission. Her goal was to identify stressors that police face and then design a stress-management course especially for them.

The class project was so successful, the deputy chief asked her to teach the course. The course was so successful, she ended up working with all six platoons in New Brunswick and with the police academy.

While still working full-time for the hospital, she continued to build her own business. She read lots of books, engaged a lawyer, and launched her business in May 1992. However, it wasn't until that November she actually named her business: "Ability Plus...". She thought long and hard about the meaning of words—and about the placement in the Yellow Pages! Her husband came up with her slogan, "Part-Time Practice, Prime-Time Delivery."

After she officially opened for business, the first person to hire her was a friend who is now a director of nursing but had at one time worked for Colleen. The director said she just wanted an inexpensive, one-hour program. And, in ten years, after Colleen had made it big, she expected her to remember who gave her her start. As her friend said, "You never forget your first." The director continues to be her staunch supporter.

Her business has grown steadily. She keeps adding business and corporate clients such as the phone company and a cable company. Recently, other health care agencies have begun hiring her.

For a nurse who was once afraid she would soon be out of work, Colleen Knudson now finds herself more work than she ever dreamed. As she puts it, "I work full time *and* part time.

FOREVER AND A DAY...

Nothing lasts forever. I remember vividly another speaker, whose star was waning, once saying to me, "Oh, sure, it's fine now but you can't be a speaker **forever**."

That comment left me reeling. Recently, the demand for my speaking services had skyrocketed. Professional speaking had become more than a way to make a living; at that moment it was literally my life. I was traveling constantly, meeting great people, basking in the limelight, and being paid outrageously well. I was flying high until that offhand comment sent me crashing back to earth.

Over the next few months the phrase, "I can't do this forever," kept replaying in my head and whenever that thought crossed my mind I felt panicky.

I had to confront the fear and put it to rest. I basically had a long talk with myself in which I said, "Hey, Mel, get a grip! First of all, when have you ever wanted to do *anything* forever? You have a short attention span. You have lots of interests and talents. So what if tomorrow you found out you couldn't be a speaker or you couldn't be a nurse, what else could you do? Hmmmmm..."

- I could be an antique dealer. I love auctions and flea markets.
- I could be a nanny.
- I could work in a toy store. Or an art gallery.
- A waitress. I'd put on a hairnet, roll my hose down and entertain the customers. I bet I'd get good tips.
- I could stand on the street corner and sing. With my lack of talent, I would have to wear a sign that said, "Put money in my cup and I'll shut up.
- I could work for an advertising agency. I'd be good at writing jingles and slogans.

• I could attach myself to a publishing house. Or write for a small-town newspaper. Heck, I could deliver newspapers!

And the list goes on... Whatever happens, I won't starve and I won't lack for things to do.

How about you? If you're a nurse who's terrified of losing your job, you need to make your own list of alternatives. There's nothing more miserable than feeling you're trapped and all out of options.

Maybe there's a phrase that keeps repeating in your mind that causes you to panic. Maybe you've heard those rumors that by the Year 2000 we'll have only half the number of hospital beds we have today.

If you've spent your whole life in acute care, you should be nervous. The hospital giveth and the hospital taketh away. If nursing is not just a way to make a living but virtually your life, your panic is understandable.

What if they close your hospital or your unit tomorrow? What then?

It's time for you to confront your fear. Don't give in to panic. Don't let your current employer or your current profession have unbridled power over you.

DIVERSIFY!

J.C. Penney said,"If all your eggs are in one basket, watch that basket!" Well, if all your eggs are in nursing's basket, you can end up staring at that basket until you're cross-eyed *or* you can start putting your eggs in other baskets just as Connie, Jessica, Colleen, and I did.

That's diversification.

That's cross-training.

That's cultivating other talents and interests.

That's keeping your wits about you.

One of the tenets of being a good negotiator is "care—

but never that much." That's important to remember as you negotiate your career.

I care about nursing. You care about nursing. But we both need to recognize that our lives can go on perfectly well without it.

Nursing may be your first choice but it should never be your only choice. Get a grip! By realizing you have a myriad of choices, you regain control.

You will not starve and you will not lack for things to do.

What Next?

1. Right now, while this is fresh in your mind, grab a pen and set your kitchen timer for five minutes. Without editing or censoring, just keep listing things you could do to make a living.

2. Set aside 10-15 minutes a day. Pick one of the phrases on this list and describe a situation in which you:

- Solved a problem
- Demonstrated leadership
- Took a risk
- Collaborated with someone from another discipline
- Enhanced teamwork
- Managed a crisis
- Saved your organization money
- Handled a complaint
- Negotiated a settlement
- Set priorities
- Resolved a conflict

3. **Write your résumé.**

4. Pick up any newspaper or magazine and see if you can identify an opportunity for nurses or nursing.

5. Keep your eyes, ears and mind open.

SEVEN YEAR ITCH

Say hello to a lot of nurses who got itchy. Some just had fantasies, some had harmless flirtations, some carried on passionate affairs, and some left their jobs and careers never to return.

Take Victoria, for example, who has just resigned her teaching position. She's feeling guilty. The director and the rest of the faculty are in a tizzy. To find a replacement for her will not be easy. They want her to stay.

She loves teaching but she's been made an offer she cannot refuse. As she puts it, "Teaching is a luxury I can no longer afford."

Victoria's been "itchy" for some time. Her salary is inadequate for her level of preparation and responsibility. For years she's watched her associate degree students begin their careers at salaries that rival hers even though she has a master's degree and twenty years of experience.

She's been moonlighting at a couple of other jobs to supplement her income and to keep her clinical skills current. Frankly, she's tired. She's tired physically, emotionally, and intellectually.

When the corporation that just hired her first winked in her direction, she resisted their advances. She wanted to be true to her school. The corporation courted her—literally wined and dined her. Any resistance she could muster wilted as they met each of her requests. The prenuptual agreement they eventually struck not only allowed her to finish out the school year; she ended up nearly doubling her old salary! (It pays to play hard to get.)

THE THRILL IS GONE

From the outside looking in, Lauren seems to have it all: a high-powered, high-prestige, high-paying job. But her restlessness is unmistakable. She's bewildered. She's worked so hard to get where she is and now she's not enjoying it.

After listening to her for awhile, I said, "You're bored." She sat silently for a moment with a bemused look on her face and then said, "You're right."

Nurses are often surprised to learn that great jobs can become just as boring as crummy jobs. It seems to happen when the learning stops.

The first year in a job is like being thrown in the deep end of the pool. You flail away. You struggle trying to keep your head above the water. You often feel like you're going down for the third time. The adrenalin pumps night and day.

By the second year, your toes touch the bottom. There's some sense of support. It doesn't take all your effort just to keep your head above water. You're a better swimmer—more efficient and effective. You can float, crawl, backstroke. You've seen these problems before. You've learned from your mistakes. You've refined your techniques.

By the third year, you glide through the water. You're on the swim team. You're winning medals.

But then, somewhere between the third and fifth year, you begin to feel waterlogged. You begin to yawn. You've seen it all before, done it all before. Same problem. Same solution. Same outcome. Next? Same problem. Same solution. Same outcome. Next? You're on autopilot. You get swimmer's itch. You want out of the pool.

Once this happens you've got to make a change in either your personal or professional life. When work settles into a comfortable routine, it can be a great time to rekindle your love life, socialize with old friends, take up a hobby, go on a dream vacation, volunteer for community service, learn to play a musical instrument, or study cultural anthropology.

Or perhaps it's time to make a change in your professional life. If you can't move up, move over.

"I don't know if it was a midlife crisis or what. Suddenly I realized I would be working another 25 years! The thought of going through the same old routines for another quarter of a century ...." Deb shuddered. "I knew I had to make a change."

"I began by asking everyone, 'Who is the best head nurse in the hospital?' Everyone gave me the same answer—Beth, Neuro ICU."

"I went to see her. I asked if she would be my mentor. She agreed."

"It's been four months now since I transfered to her unit. I feel alive again. Nursing's exciting just like it was when I was a new grad. I've had momentary doubts. I've had some terrifying experiences. But I'm learning so much. And there's so much more to learn! I could never go back."

The good news is, if you change specialties in nursing like Deb did, you won't have to go back to Square One in terms of salary. The bad news is you will have to go back to Square One in terms of being a novice. It may take months or years to recapture that smug expert feeling you enjoyed in your old specialty. If you're contemplating such a move, you'll take comfort in reading Patricia Benner's **From Novice to Expert**.

As uncomfortable as transitions like this are, it may be less painful than staying put. As Deb said, inspite of some doubts and terrifying moments, "I could never go back."

Changing specialties or changing jobs is difficult enough. If you decide to change careers, be prepared to start over—at the bottom—or don't bother. Be prepared to struggle, to squirm.

A friend of mine returned to school to get a more "practical" degree than her one in fine arts. This time she majored in graphic design. At her graduation party, we all admired her portfolio. Shannon is very talented.

Unfortunately, her job search had proven disappointing. After months of interviewing, she had only been offered entry-level positions. She dismissed those opportunities saying, "An entry-level position is all right when you're in your twenties, but not in your forties! The long hours. The low pay. I don't think so."

Poor Shannon. She didn't get the memo. The one that says if you change careers, you don't get to start at the top. You have to start at the bottom and work your way up. You have to pay your dues. It doesn't matter how old you are. Because she's unwilling to start over, she's doomed to go nowhere fast. Her new degree won't work for her if she's not prepared to work for it.

BREAKING THE MOLD

Her business card reads, "Reynolds & Associates: Marketing * Advertising * Public Relations." There's no hint of nursing. Yet Nancy Reynolds spent years as a nurse working with new moms and babies.

Feeling restless, she eventually went back to school and got a master's degree in guidance and counselling. Maybe that's when she began to realize she was in the wrong profession.

Nursing seemed so rigid. There was only one right way to do things. Creativity was not rewarded. In fact, it was often punished. She felt "stifled, squashed." As Nancy puts it, she "just didn't fit the mold of nursing."

She went to a career counselor in the alumni office who helped her get back in touch with her true self. Nancy was encouraged to think about what she really loved doing. In high school she had been artistic and poetic. She loved to write.

Then the counselor gave her a battery of tests such as Strong-Campbell and Myers-Briggs which basically confirmed what she already suspected. She belongs in marketing, advertising, or interior design.

The counselor suggested she talk with other people who did this kind of work. Nancy also enrolled in Public Relations 101. She proceeded to take a course each term such as media relations and creative strategy in advertising. She created a portfolio and did a work/study internship with an advertising agency.

But working full time with four children (one in college), Nancy knew it would take forever to complete yet another degree. And even if she did, it would be tough breaking into public relations/advertising in the conventional way. She knew if she went to work for someone else, she would have to start at the bottom and pay her dues all over again.

Feeling confident she could do this on her own, she opened her own agency. She vowed to start small and work into this new career under he own steam and at her own speed. It took a few years to complete the transition.

But Reynolds & Associates has not forgotten its roots. Today, about half Nancy's business comes from health-care organizations. In addition, some of her favorite clients are individual nurses.

As she counsels other nurses who are "edging toward entrepreneurship," she draws on her guidance background as well as her advertising/marketing skills. Nancy helps them clarify exactly what they want to do. She urges them to consider work that would be fun.

When her fledgling nurse entrepreneurs meet resistance or encounter obstacles, she knows they often lack the confidence to push ahead. She challenges them with three questions: Who says you can't? Why not? Who cares?

Nancy's had her share of ups and downs. She encourages other nurses to put failure into perspective. After all, she tells them, it's not a matter of life or death. She recalls Chrysler Corporation's Lee Iacocca saying to someone who accused him of failing, "So what? If I don't fail, I'm not learning." She shares his view that failing is often a prerequisite for success.

In 1991 Nancy founded South Carolina Nurses in Business with the motto, "Nurses Doing Business with Nurses." Each year the organization sponsors an educational seminar where nurses can network and tour exhibits. She calls it her "missionary project." That seems appropriate. Nancy is definitely a nurse with a mission.

NEVER SAY NEVER

In high school Judith Miller vowed there were two things she would never be—a nurse or a teacher. You guessed it. She's both.

After serving in the Army Nurse Corps and working in public health, she got her master's degree. While she loved nursing, she found she was "happiest in front of a classroom." When her children were young, she taught part time.

Unfortunately, part-time faculty are often "used and abused." The college kept adding to her workload, but not to her salary. When she realized what a piddly amount she was making per hour, she resigned.

Shortly afterward, the college approached her about tutoring students who couldn't pass state boards. She jumped at the chance.

For the next few years, she tutored students in her home. She loved it. She had found her niche.

She might still be tutoring in her home today if her students hadn't had so much trouble finding the recommended textbooks. They were wasting precious hours running from bookstore to bookstore often without success.

She wanted to offer the books for sale but to *sell* anything she would need a license. And a bookstore, no matter how small or how specialized,would not be allowed as a home occupation.

Judith decided to venture forth. She "left home" and rented a place where she could have both a classroom and a bookstore. Today her company, Nursing Tutorial and Consulting Services, is thriving in Annandale, Virginia.

She specializes in helping graduate nurses and nursing students pass tests including everything from certification to state boards. Her company provides classes, workshops, and tutors. The bookstore carries audio and video tapes, and basic supplies like stethoscopes and scissors.

Judith's business continues to expand and diversify. She has so much fun teaching, she thought students should have just as much fun learning. That's why she began to create teaching aids like the Acid-Base Game and the Fluid-Electrolyte Game.

Are you having fun in your career? Judith is.

FUN & G.A.M.E.S.

That reminds me of another nurse devoted to making learning fun. Her name is Michele Deck. After years of working in labor and delivery, she developed an independent Lamaze practice. She taught four classes a week for ten years.

When her husband, Brian, was transferred to Mississippi, she continued to work in New Orleans even though it meant a long commute. Her salary was more than double what it would have been if she had worked closer to home.

During this time they had two children and Michele began working on her master's degree in adult education. By then she was also working in staff development.

Her creativity, energy, and teaching ability were a winning combination. She didn't just teach a class, she gave a performance. While she was "performing" at a conference, she was "discovered" by Bob Pike.

As Michele tells it, this "suit" kept wandering in and out of her session. When she finished, he shook her hand and said, "You need to write a book and I'm going to publish it!" He sent her a contract. He was so impressed he asked her to come work for him as a consultant. Bob Pike trains trainers.

In her classes Michele always used props, toys, gimmicks, gadgets, and games which she picked up in dime stores, gift shops, and even yard sales. The trainers she was training loved it. They were clamoring to know where she found all that great stuff.

Recognizing a new opportunity, Michele began providing props for trainers and educators. Brian left his job in banking to man the home front and to grow the new business. Today Tool Thyme for Trainers is flourishing in Metairie, Louisiana.

Where can you find squiggle balls, creativity kits, cartoon books, word games, timers, pointers, crazy dice, and tips on being a great presenter? Call for their catalog!

Michele went from being a nurse to being a certified childbirth educator to being an author, trainer, and entrepreneur. Who knows what she'll get the itch to do next?

ENTREPRENEURIAL SEIZURES

At one time I owned a small art gallery which I treated like a hobby instead of a business. My hours were erratic and I was my own best customer. But it amused me. And, as long as the gallery didn't lose money or interfer with the rest of my life, I was happy.

An opportunity arose to participate in a women-in-business trade fair. It was sponsored by the Small Business Administration at a local hotel. For a mere $20 I could have breakfast, listen to a speaker, and set up a booth to display my wares. Several impressive corporations were co-sponsoring the event and promised to send representatives to tour the exhibits.

It sounded like a good opportunity. I reasoned that someone had to supply artwork to decorate all their office buildings. Why not me?

Breakfast was great. The speaker was even better. That's where I first learned that 90% of all small businesses fail in the first year and 95% fail in the first five years. Looking at myself and the other exhibitors, I began to understand why that was true.

Even more startling was my realization that even if we succeeded, our "success" would be insignificant. The potential for greatness just wasn't there.

With a couple of exceptions, all fifty of us were engaged in trivial pursuits. It was a questionable assortment of beauty shop owners, caterers, and women who made knitting their life's work. My booth was sandwiched between a poodle groomer and an escort service.

At 10 a.m. sharp the corporate representatives dutifully traipsed through the exhibits barely glancing to the right or left. By 10:30 a.m all had vanished. Only two women attracted any attention: one selling industrial-strength grinders and another with high-powered solvents guaranteed to eat through concrete.

There was nothing to do but pack up and go home.

Later I realized the corporations were all government contractors being pressured to include minority and women-owned businesses among their suppliers. By sponsoring the event, no one could accuse them of not making an effort to comply with the law. Was it their fault that women's businesses had nothing to offer? No.

Until that day I had never thought about how silly some women's businesses are. We are dreamers but few of us dream big. Our business ventures are pretty but not practical.

Many of us suffer from what author Michael E. Gerber would call an *entrepreneurial seizure*. His excellent book, **The E Myth Revisited: Why Most Small Businesses Fail and What to Do**

About It, is must reading for any nurse thinking of going into business. It will help you avoid lots of pitfalls. For example, he cautions readers not to make *the fatal assumption* that "If you understand the technical work of a business, you understand a business that does technical work." He warns that being self-employed can become "the worst job in the world because you're working for a lunatic!"

Amen.

If you're thinking about going into business for yourself, take a long, hard look at your earning potential. Do the numbers.

A nurse approached me at a conference. She said she wanted to get out of nursing but had no idea of what else she could do. When I asked her what she really enjoyed doing, she thought for a long time and then said, "I like to sew."

A hobby may point the way to another career. However, when a hobby becomes "work" it might cease to be fun. Remember, a hobby is meant for relaxation, not revenue generation.

While some people do make their living sewing, few of them make anything close to what a nurse makes. How realistic would a career in sewing be? It wouldn't be difficult to research.

DOING THE NUMBERS

Before Cathy Williams bought a health-care employment franchise from Health Force, Inc., she did her homework. Her research suggested 10% of recently discharged patients require additional care at home and that the average cost of that care is about $2000 per patient.

She then called the Colorado Hospital Association to learn how many patients were discharged annually in the Denver Metropolitan area. She estimated her local market to be $34 million!

When she checked the telephone book, she found fifty competitors listed. So she enrolled in the University of Denver's Small Business Institute to learn how to beat the competition. Her goal: to capture 10% of that $34 million dollar market.

MAKING THE PIECES FIT

Susan McLaughlin's career resembles a crazy quilt. She has several academic degrees including a Ph.D. from Harvard. She's been everything from a school teacher to an urban planner to a health care consultant to a home health nurse. But today she owns a quilt shop, Capital Quilts, in Gaithersburg, Maryland.

In an earlier life, this well-educated, well-paid consultant dealt with health manpower. When clients asked her if she was a nurse, she felt uncomfortable. She felt her advice "rang hollow" because she didn't know the technical side of health care first hand.

As luck would have it, or should I say as bad luck would have it, both she and her husband were laid off on the same day. That's when she decided to go to nursing school. This woman with four degrees had never had a science course. While Harvard might waive requirements, community colleges do not. But she loved nursing school. In some ways it was her most difficult course of study. She found nurses had a totally different way of thinking.

After graduation she went to work in a hospital. She wanted to *know* what it was to be a nurse. But she found patients in acute care too sick, too scared, too hurting. After a year she switched to home health. It was just her cup of tea.

But after eight years she itched to do something else. The community college was looking for a nursing school director. She applied but was turned down because she didn't have a higher degree in nursing. It wasn't the first time she had encountered one of the "artificial barriers nursing loves to create." She fears nursing has "focused too long and hard on *the one right way*."

Four years earlier Susan had become involved in quilting. Her quilting colleagues were bemoaning the fact that the local quilt store had been closed for a year and the fabric stores rarely carried supplies serious quilters need.

Susan had one of those entrepreneurial seizures.

As she rattles off statistics about quilters, you can see how thoroughly she researched her new business. She visited every quilt shop within 500 miles and took classes offered by the Small Business Administration. She wanted to make sure she knew how to handle the business of being in business. Capital Quilts has been open for almost two years and is going strong.

Susan wears out careers faster than other people wear out shoes. Recently, when her supportive, but slightly exhausted husband and children plaintively asked, "What's next?"

She smiled and replied, "Law school?"

BEFORE YOU QUIT YOUR DAY JOB

Things were changing and not for the better. The hospital where Joann Savage had worked in labor and delivery for ten years merged and "suffered" a corporate takeover. The nurses were no longer autonomous, collaborative practice disappeared, and loyal long-time employees were being told to "clean out their lockers."

Driving home she passed a strip mall in her neighborhood and saw a man putting a "For Rent" sign in one of the storefronts. She veered off the road, slammed on her brakes, jumped out of the car, and asked him "How much?" She dashed home and came back with a check for $300.

Then she called her best friend, Pat, and said, "We're going into business." For years she'd had an itch to open a second-hand children's clothing store. She had met Pat through the community theater and the two of them had spent hours daydreaming about going into business together.

Suddenly they were in business. What next? First stop was the library. They checked out every book they could find on starting a business. They got advice from the Service Core of Retired Executives (SCORE). They went to the university where an intern helped set up their business for free. Joann and Pat each put in $1500 and formed a legal partnership. Within five weeks they had their license. Within two months they opened their doors.

Incidently, two months before Pat had been laid off from her job. It was a case of perfect timing. And they were the perfect team.

Joann describes them as an "innie and an outie." Pat had the bookkeeping, organizational, and business skills to make it work from the inside. Joann, whom Pat calls "Mayor of the City" because she knows everyone, had the public relations and marketing ability to bring people in from the outside. She was great at rounding up people to consign items and customers to buy them.

Both share a flair for the dramatic and are highly creative. They believe presentation is everything. The decor is so wonderful, they have to remind customers the clothing is secondhand. They also handle toys, furniture, car seats, anything to do with kids.

Amazed customers quickly spread the word and business trippled in less than three years. Clothespins ("Let your clothes hang out with us") had to move into a bigger space. The number of people consigning items rose from 15 to 300!

Clothespins was a success—a *qualified* success. Joann and Pat didn't exactly quit their day jobs. They knew this venture wouldn't make them rich. What it did do was give them rich experience. Although they each took home less than $1000 a month, they now had more control over their schedules and half of their worklife. Knowing they wouldn't fire or lay themselves off made them feel more secure and self-sufficient. A major benefit was being able to involve the whole family in the venture. Both had school-age children who helped with sorting, tagging, and cleaning.

Soon after renting the storefront, Joann left the hospital. She took a per diem job doing stress testing but that didn't work out. Then an obstetrician asked her to fill in for his office nurse. Three years later she was still "filling in" two days a week and working at Clothespins three days a week. When her children go to college, she thinks she might return to school herself and become a midwife. Pat's other job involves data entry and customer service for a trucking company. Both love their work and their business.

THE ONE THAT GOT AWAY

Another nurse who kept her day job while she prepared for a complete career change was Diann Garfield. She began college at Fresno State as a biology major. When she realized there were no jobs in that field, she switched her major to nursing. She sat for state boards while finishing her degree in biology.

Diann worked in a burn unit and then an open-heart surgical unit. But when her husband was transferred to rural Pennsylvania, she found she had to commute thirty miles and work nights just for a mundane nursing job. She began to tire of the low pay, low status, and poor working conditions that plagued nursing at that time. She was young and knew she had many years of work ahead of her. She couldn't see staying in nursing for a lifetime. She itched to change careers.

When they moved to Charlottesville, Virginia, she got her chance. She went back to school and became an electrical engineer!

At first glance it seems like a radical departure. But if you take a second look, it was a logical switch. Diann had grown up in a family of engineers. There was always scientific talk around the house. The only thing that kept her from becoming an engineer in the first place was the way women in such male-dominated fields were treated.

Age and experience gave her the maturity and self-confidence she needed to pursue her first love. Today she works in satellite communications and is very happy she made the change.

DR. BABY PROOFER IS A NURSE

Thomas B. Golden, an emergency nurse, saw a need and filled it. Distressed by the numbers of infants and toddlers coming into the ER, he knew he had to do something to prevent these tragedies.

In doing the research for his business, he learned that accidents in the home kill more children than all childhood diseases combined. He also learned that 90% of all pediatric trauma is preventable and that 60% of infant-toddler accident prevention is education.

So he built a business based on prevention and education. He goes into homes and evaluates the risk factors. Then he shares his findings with the parents. They can either take corrective action themselves or they can hire him to do the actual "baby-proofing."

He will go in and install things like proper latches, outlet covers, gates, and mesh between stair railings to keep babies from falling through or getting their heads stuck.

As his business grew, he needed to find good part-time help. He found EMTs to be the perfect solution. They had knowledge, experience, motivation, and schedules that allowed them to moonlight.

This entrepreneurial nurse has expanded his operation in two areas. First, as Tom reviewed and tested the safety products on the market, he found many of them promised far more than they delivered. Worse, some things he needed weren't available at all. He began to design and market some devices himself.

Second, he realized a lot of other nurses might be interested in becoming what he calls "pediatric traumatologists." He developed an intensive, interactive, five-day course. He not only teaches the specifics of baby-proofing but dispenses information essential to running a successful business: practical stuff like developing a business plan, marketing advice, as well as billing and collection techniques.

A LITTLE SOMETHING ON THE SIDE

When Ronald Bolen, Jr., graduated from a nursing program at James Madison University in May 1994, he assumed he'd have a job. After all, his Veterans Administration scholarship obligated him to two years of service.

The VA, however, had no openings at the moment and he had to go job hunting elsewhere. Although Ron was a brand-new RN, he had been an EMT for three years and a Shock-Trauma Technician for two years . That's probably what helped him land a job in the emergency room of a private hospital.

That hospital had a task force charged with finding ways to build better working relationships between the rescue squads and the emergency room personnel. One of their suggestions was a newsletter. Ron volunteered. His computer skills and interest in desktop publishing resulted in "Vital Signs."

After working for the hospital only six months, the VA summoned Ron. They had an opening in West Virginia. While he was busy packing up his family for the move, he was also busy training colleagues to take over publishing the popular newsletter.

You would think a new home, new baby (Conner), and a new job as evening charge nurse in a step-down ICU / Medical - Surgical unit would keep Ron more than busy but he missed doing the newsletter. He had an itch to learn about publishing. So he answered an ad.

A local publisher was looking for a part-time person with Macintosh experience to do graphic design and pre-press work. Ron convinced him he was a hard worker and a quick learner. He got the job. He works mornings for the publisher and evenings for the hospital. (By the way, check the opening credits. Ron did the pre-press work on this book.)

One day Ron approached the publisher about also being their "safety officer." It turns out small businesses can get substantial reductions in insurance premiums if they have a medically trained person on site even a few hours a week. Ron seized the opportunity.

What does a safety officer do? Ron began by revamping the first aid station. He got rid of extraneous equipment and supplies which were outmoded, useless, and even potentially dangerous. He streamlined everything while making sure to meet the requirements of OSHA (Occupational Safety and Health Administration). And he saved the company a lot of money in the process!

Ron has also saved the company money by counseling employees and making appropriate referrals. For example, emergency room visits are expensive. Many times the employee can be directed to use a mini-clinic or make a doctor's appointment instead.

He keeps records and documents results. He teaches CPR and first aid. He tracks problems like absenteeism. He screens the environment and conducts surveys. In short, Ron identifies problems and solves them. Like the time he noticed the folks in the mailing room were consuming bottles of Tylenol. When he visited that work site he found it hot, stuffy, and noisy. By installing a couple of fans and providing earplugs, the headaches were virtually eliminated.

Ron has already been asked to consult as a safety officer for other companies. He thinks it would be possible to work on a retainer basis and build quite a nice business. He also sees this as a way for entrepreneurial nurses to barter for health insurance.

Many nurses who would like to open their own businesses are stopped cold by the fear of losing their fringe benefits, especially health care. If you served as safety officer for some company, you could be covered under their policy as part of your compensation. Or, Ron thinks you could approach a major insurance company and offer to do some troubleshooting in exchange for benefits.

As for Ron, he has so many talents and interests, it is impossible to predict what he will be doing after he finishes his stint at the VA hospital. One of the publisher's clients who has three weekly newspapers is talking with him about writing a health section. Ron wants to call it "Nursing Notes." He can also see using his art and design skills to give more pizazz to bland nursing publications. Another possibility would be a joint venture with his wife, Jackie, who's a teacher, to make health information fun and accessible to children. And in addition to all this, he is in the Army Reserves, volunteers as a Paramedic, and wants to be a flight nurse!

COMING UP WITH THE SCRATCH

Dreams do come true. Let me tell you a great rags-to-riches story. It's about how Patricia Kathleen Scheerle, better know as P.K., became president, CEO, and sole proprietor of American Nursing Services Inc., a company that currently employs about 2000 nurses and generates revenues of over $10 million a year.

It began in 1980 when a couple of twentysomething associate degree nurses, P.K. and her best friend, Margaret Candon, left Vermont with all their worldly goods packed in a two-seater

Fiat. They had an itch to see California. Their directions must have been to head for the Gulf and hang a right.

By the time they reached New Orleans, they had run out of money. So they decided to work a few days, earn a few bucks, and continue on. But something unexpected happened. They fell in love with New Orleans. In fact, they're both still there.

When P.K. first arrived in New Orleans, she went to work for a rent-a-nurse agency. After a couple days on the job, they offered her the director of nursing position. That should have been her cue to run, not walk, toward the nearest exit. She lasted six months. By that time she had discovered their way of running a business was not her way.

She joined another temporary agency and returned to her first love, pediatric ICU. Within days her new boss, who had been impressed with the way she'd run the competitor's agency, called her in and asked her to run his company. Eight months later her boss sold out. The new owners didn't impress P.K. She made preparations to leave.

The Certified Public Accountant who had negotiated the buyout approached her. He offered to co-sign a loan so they could start their own company. At first she thought he was crazy but he convinced her she could do it. He won her over by suggesting she could spearhead a company in which nursing would govern itself.

That last idea was irrestible to P.K. Like most nurses she was itching to see changes in the profession. She wanted nurses to have more respect, more money, more autonomy, and more control. In fact, P.K., Maggie, and a half dozen other renegade nurses used to gather after work to sip margaritas and dream of running their own agency. Opportunity was knocking. It was time to put up or shut up.

So in 1982, P.K. and the CPA incorporated American Nursing Services and began providing supplemental staff to ICUs. Projected revenues for their first year had been $400,000 but they did $1,300,000 in billings!

Then the bottom fell out. On their first anniversary, the CPA's priorities suddenly changed and he wanted out of the partnership. The bank abruptly called the note. P.K. had 48 hours to raise $160,000 or watch all her hard work and dreams go down the drain. She put on her navy blue suit and went to eight banks. They all turned her down.

She made a list of the richest people she knew. The first one on the list was a doctor. He was intrigued by the idea. He said he wanted Price-Waterhouse to examine her books. If they agreed it was a good investment, she could count him in. She told him not to drag his feet. The bank's clock was ticking.

Price-Waterhouse gave an enthusiastic thumbs-up. The doctor wanted 51 percent. P.K. said no. She told him it was 50-50 or nothing. He agreed to be her silent partner.

But two years later, with money rolling in, the doctor decided he didn't want to be silent anymore. He tried to pull rank. He was a doctor. She was just a nurse. They locked horns.

He gave her 30 days to buy him out. If she couldn't come up with the money, he would buy her out. Once again she put on her navy blue suit, took the company's books, and headed for the banks. The first bank she called on gave her the loan. She bought out the doctor in February 1985 and has been the sole owner ever since.

As *the* boss P.K. saw her dreams now become an 80-hour-a-week reality. She built a solid reputation by never making a commitment she couldn't keep, even if it meant turning down a lucrative contract. She only hired nurses with impeccable credentials, "ones you would want taking care of your own parents." She stressed image and professionalism. She set up educational programs.

P.K. has always been a champion of nurses and nursing. To give you an example, nurses who were interviewed but not hired by ANS because they didn't have the right stuff were invited to take educational programs and buddy with senior critical care nurses to bring their skills up to speed. All this was provided free of charge.

Today her company not only provides nurses to hundreds of hospitals, it provides nursing staff at events ranging from the Olympics to the Republican National Convention. It answers offbeat calls too like the one from a Japanese ship in the Gulf of Mexico requesting a nurse to give 30 cholera injections. ANS dispatched a nurse on a helicopter.

The company has expanded into surrounding states of Texas and Florida. It has added other professionals to its roster such as respiratory, occupational, and physical therapists. And P.K. is always itching to do more.

She volunteers with organizations such as the Red Cross and Junior Achievement. She serves on boards, chairs committees, and organizes benefits.

As with most self-taught, self-made people, P.K. always has her antenna up. She learns from every person, from every experience. For example, a casual conversation over cocktails led her to an unbelievable educational opportunity.

She was hobnobbing with the New Orleans business elite at a charitable affair when a man asked where she had gone to business school. She replied she hadn't. She had gone to nursing school. Increduous, the man asked how many business courses she had taken. None. How many business books had she read? Oh, she read all the best-sellers. No, he meant business textbooks. None.

"You have to go back to school," he said.

P.K. groaned. She told him she got the same back-to-school pressure from nursing. It wasn't that she didn't have an itch to learn, but going back to school seemed totally out of the question. She couldn't put a multi-million dollar business on hold.

Then he said, "You should apply to Harvard."

Harvard? Yes. It seems Harvard has a very innovative program for executives. To be eligible you have to have the title of president, employ at least 100 people, and generate revenues of $5 million a year. He told her Harvard was always on the lookout for women because so few met the criteria.

P.K. applied to Harvard and was accepted!

Move over, Cinderella. An associate degree nurse got into Harvard Business School!

She went one month a year for three years in a total immersion program with 119 other company presidents from 52 countries. She says it was a phenomenal learning experience. She made fast friends and business contacts for life. (By the way, there were only six women in the class.)

You'll be happy to learn that P.K. not only works hard, she plays hard. She loves to party and thought there ought to be a big bash to celebrate nursing and recognize outstanding nurses. That itch of hers resulted in "The Great 100." Launched in 1986 this lavish gala honors 100 nurses nominated by their peers. While friends, families, and colleagues feast on gourmet goodies donated by New Orleans' top chefs, thousands of dollars are raised for nursing scholarships.

In all the years P.K. has missed only one "Great 100" celebration which brings me to the best of the story. After a long courtship, a thirtysomething P.K. finally said "yes" to Bruce Bolyard, a commercial real estate broker, and one of the nicest men on Planet Earth. On April 19, 1995, P.K. became a fortysomething primipara. Believe it or not, Elizabeth Eloise was born on "Great 100 Day."

I once asked Maggie, who is still P.K.'s closest friend as well as head of ANS's travel nurse division, why it was that of all the nurses who met regularly to dream and brainstorm, P.K. was the one who ended up with all the marbles. Maggie said simply, "Because when it came right down to it, P.K. was the only one willing to sign her name on the bottom line."

I guess that will always be the difference between the doers and the dreamers.

Everyday I meet nurses with an itch. But they want someone else to provide the scratch.

Everyday I meet nurses sitting beside the highway of life waiting for opportunity to come along. It doesn't work that way. You've got to hit the road like P.K. did. You've got to be willing to go the distance.

What Next?

1. Are you staying where you are for love or for money?

2. Is it time to:

_____ Stay put
_____ Move up
_____ Move over
_____ Move out

3. Which of the nurses you met in this chapter inspired you? What did you learn from them? What ideas did you get?

4. If you were to have an *entrepreneurial seizure*, what sort of business would you create?

My stars! You could be the first nurse on Mars!

KISS OFF

Just when I thought I'd heard everything, I ran across a happy-ending article in one of the popular weekly magazines. It was a follow-up piece on a scam which had bilked hundreds of men out of thousands of dollars.

The man pictured was one who had contributed generously to a "revirginization" project which claimed to somehow recycle fallen women and make them virgins again. While the poor fool didn't get his money back, he was about to marry one of the wayward women he had tried to revirginate.

I absolutely convulsed with laughter which was embarrassing because at the time I was on an airplane. It took me quite awhile to regain my composure. Later I began to think of something Erik Erickson once wrote about people living in trailers because they didn't want to make any irreversible decisions.

Perhaps one measure of maturity is the ability to make irreversible decisions and to live in peace with the outcome.

As I encourage nurses to explore all options, to seize opportunities inside and outside of traditional nursing, I can feel their excitement mount...and their fear.

After I share some of the unexpected twists and turns my own career path has taken, I am struck by the number of nurses who ask me if I can go back. They want to know if I could ever go back and be a *real nurse* again.

Their question shouldn't surprise me. It's one I asked myself frequently when I took those first tentative steps off the beaten path. For a long time I tried to leave a trail of bread crumbs. I wanted to make sure I could find my way back.

But now I've gone too far.

Unlike revirginization, it's not impossible but it's not probable. It would be like trying to put toothpaste back in the tube. Again, it's not impossible but it would be extremely difficult, awfully messy, and not the least bit cost effective.

So please don't ask me if I can go back. Rather ask me, "What next?"

You are holding the answer in your hands. With this book I become an official publisher. Do you remember when I was going through a career crisis and was making a "What I Want" list? One item was "to have publishing experience not just writing experience."

When I wrote that statement, a seed was planted. Its growth has been slow but steady. First I published posters and notecards for nurses. Then I added a coloring book titled "I Might Be a Nurse" designed to teach children about the many roles nurses play. (You've seen some of the illustrations from the coloring book scattered throughout this text.) Now it's this career planner — a genuine book published by my own Pro-Nurse Press.

It will be introduced in St. Louis at a huge trade show sponsored by the National Association of College Stores (NACS). I will be an exhibitor.

When they assigned me a booth, I asked where Mosby would be. As far as I'm concerned, Mosby is the best publisher of nursing books including three I authored. And besides, Mosby would be the only "person" I knew at this party. I was told they would occupy an eight-booth island in Publishers Row.

My little booth, on the other hand, would be on the outskirts of the convention center, lost among hundreds of others selling gifts, gizmos, and gadgets to bookstore managers.

When I asked if I could move to Publishers Row, I was told it was out of NACS' control. I would have to contact the Association of American Publishers (AAP) and see if I met their criteria. The AAP not only let me into Publishers Row, they invited me to join their association! I figure that makes me a *real* publisher.

The best part is my booth will be right across the aisle from Mosby.

Mosby is the oak. I am the acorn.

Mosby has 1200 authors. I have one — but I'm gaining on them.

How long will I pursue this path? I don't know. Where will it take me? I don't know. I don't have all the answers. I never did. No one ever does. So don't waste your time asking me or anyone else what you should do. Ask yourself. You are the expert. And remember, you don't need all the answers. You just need one. The answer to the question...

What Next?